TOXIC STRESS
AND
THE TWENTIETH CENTURY
BLUES

VERNON COLEMAN

WHAT THE PAPERS SAY ABOUT
DR VERNON COLEMAN

Dr Vernon Coleman's books have been translated into 14 languages and sold in just about every country in the world. Here are some comments about him and his previous books from the British Press:

'Britain's leading health care campaigner' – THE SUN

'The sharpest mind in medical journalism' – THE STAR

'Dr Coleman writes with more sense than bias' – DAILY EXPRESS

'GP turned author whose concern is providing the layman with good advice on a variety of subjects' – YORKSHIRE POST

'Dr Coleman has in recent years challenged accepted ideas about everything from beauty products to more strictly medical matters' – THE SCOTSMAN

'Outspoken and alert observer' – SUNDAY EXPRESS

'He is a fluent writer, all commonsense and no nonsense' – HEALTH SERVICES MANAGEMENT

'GP turned columnist whose writings send the medical establishment into a flat spin' – EXPRESS AND STAR

'The most influential medical writer in Britain. There can be little doubt that Vernon Coleman is the people's doctor' – DEVON LIFE

'The medical expert you can't ignore' – SUNDAY INDEPENDENT

'The doctor who dares to speak his mind' – OXFORD MAIL

'Man with a mission' – MORNING NEWS

'Dr Coleman is more illuminating than the proverbial lady with the lamp' – COMPANY MAGAZINE

'One of the country's leading medical authors' – THE TIMES

'Dr Coleman has the gift of being able to sweeten the bitter pill of knowledge ... presenting revolutionary concepts in words everyone can understand' – EVENING TELEGRAPH

'Refreshingly sensible' – SPECTATOR

'Dr Coleman gains in stature with successive books' – COVENTRY EVENING TELEGRAPH

'He has a racy and lucid style and he successfully combines the gifts of a journalist and of a perspicacious reader' – WORLD MEDICINE

'He writes lucidly and wittily' – GOOD HOUSEKEEPING

'A writer with the common touch ... his humour masks deep thinking about subjects which interest him' – YORKSHIRE EVENING POST

'The patient's champion. The doctor with the common touch' – BIRMINGHAM POST

'Dr Coleman has a string of successful titles to his credit and the outspoken, sometimes controversial and often humorous attitude he brings to writing has done much to enhance his reputation' – WARWICKSHIRE AND WORCESTERSHIRE LIFE

'Clear and helpful' – THE GUARDIAN

'Vernon Coleman is a leading medical authority and known to millions through his writing, broadcasting and best selling books' – WOMANS OWN

'His message is important' – THE ECONOMIST

'It is always stimulating to read Vernon Coleman' – THE LIBERATOR

'Its impossible not to be impressed' – WESTERN DAILY PRESS

'A persuasive writer whose arguments, based on research and experience, are sound' – NURSING STANDARD

'Refreshingly forthright' – LIVERPOOL DAILY POST

'You can always rely on Dr Coleman for frank advice' – OVER 21

'Not a man to pull his punches' – SUNDAY MERCURY

'Vernon Coleman has written many highly informative books for the general public' – TRUE MAGAZINE

'Dr Coleman's study will do much to enlighten not only the medical profession but also every man' – BOOKS AND BOOKMEN

'His book Bodypower' is one of the most sensible treatises on personal survival that has ever been published' – YORKSHIRE EVENING POST

'His wise handbook 'Stress Control' is a bible for those who wish to understand and combat stress' – COMPANY

'Britain's leading medical author' – THE STARS AND STRIPES

'Dr Coleman is crusading for a more complete awareness of what is good and bad for our bodies. In the course of that he has made many friends and some powerful enemies' – WESTERN MORNING NEWS

'His advice is practical and readable' – THE NORTHERN ECHO

'His advice is optimistic and enthusiastic' – BRITISH MEDICAL JOURNAL

'Dr Coleman is one medic who doesn't beat about the bush' – NEW WOMAN

'Dr Coleman speaks openly and reassuringly' – OXFORD TIMES

'Hurrah, then for Dr Vernon Coleman' – SHEFFIELD TELEGRAPH

'One of Britain's leading experts' – SLIMMER MAGAZINE

'Acknowledged authority' – THE OBSERVER

'Dr Coleman has a maverick reputation for his writings on the tactics of the drug industry and his questioning of some established medical treatments' – SUNDAY TIMES

'Merciless' – EVENING TIMES, GLASGOW

'His advice is clear and commonsensible' – EVENING NEWS

'What he says ... is true' – PUNCH

'He is keenly aware of the social dimensions of medical practice' – TIMES LITERARY SUPPLEMENT

Vernon Coleman has a common sense and practical approach to providing answers for real people living lives they can't totally control' – WEIGHT WATCHERS

'Dr Coleman lays about him with an uncompromising verbal scalpel, dipped in vitriol, against all sorts of sacred cows' – EXETER EXPRESS AND ECHO

'Dr Coleman has thoroughly and unerringly investigated and published the workings of the health service' – FITNESS MAGAZINE

'Dr Coleman ... has a string of medical bestsellers to his name' – HEALTH SERVICE JOURNAL

'Has done more to undermine the establishment's use of Aids to promote fear and insecurity ... than the whole of the left' – LIVING MARXISM

'Coleman presses on persuasively (and) provides thought provoking ideas' – CONSERVATIVE NEWSPAPER

'Dr Coleman manages to present complex technical arguments in a simple and understandable way ... he argues very cogently and convincingly ... what he says is valid and needs to be said' – NURSING TIMES

'A godsend' – DAILY TELEGRAPH

TOXIC STRESS
AND
THE TWENTIETH CENTURY
BLUES

How to deal with the unseen forces which make you work hard doing things you don't like and which encourage you to make yourself ill saving up to buy things you don't really need.

VERNON COLEMAN

By the same author

on medicine

The Medicine Men
Paper Doctors
Everything You Want to Know About Ageing
Stress Control
The Home Pharmacy
Aspirin or Ambulance
Face Values
Stress and Your Stomach
Guilt
The Good Medicine Guide
A Guide to Child Health
Bodypower
An A to Z of Women's Problems
Bodysense
Taking Care of Your Skin
Life Without Tranquillisers
High Blood Pressure
Diabetes
Arthritis
Eczema and Dermatitis
The Story of Medicine
Natural Pain Control
Mindpower
Addicts and Addictions
Dr Vernon Coleman's Guide to Alternative Medicine
Stress Management Techniques
Overcoming Stress
The 20 Minute Health Check
Know Yourself
The Health Scandal
Sex for Everyone
Mind Over Body
Eat Green – Lose Weight

on cricket

Thomas Winsden's Cricketing Almanack
Diary of a Cricket Lover
The Village Cricket Tour

as Edward Vernon

Practice Makes Perfect
Practise What You Preach
Getting Into Practice
Aphrodisiacs – an Owner's Manual
The Complete Guide to Life

as Marc Charbonnier

Tunnel

TOXIC STRESS
AND
THE TWENTIETH CENTURY
BLUES

VERNON COLEMAN

CHILTON DESIGNS

Chilton Designs Publishers
Preston House, Kentisbury, Barnstaple, Devon EX31 4NH

First published in the United Kingdom by Chilton Designs in 1991.

Reprinted 1993

Set by B.P. Integraphics, Avon
Printed by The Bath Press, Avon

British Library Cataloguing in Publication Data
Coleman, Vernon, *1946–*
    Toxic stress: and the twentieth century blues.
    1. Man. Stress
    I. Title
    155.9042

ISBN 0–9503527–4–8

THE PARADOX

Superficially, we live in a wealthy, civilised society. We have motorways, nuclear power, colour television, supersonic aeroplanes, vitamin pills and microwave ovens. We have motor cars which remind us to put on our seat belts. We have central heating systems which automatically turn on when the temperature falls. Surgeons can transplant hearts, livers, lungs, kidneys and pieces of brain. Smallpox has been eradicated.

But, below the surface and almost out of sight, our society is sicker than ever before.

The incidence of baby battering is on the increase.

The number of marriages ending in divorce goes up annually.

The incidence of child abuse is increasing dramatically.

The incidence of serious mental illness is increasing rapidly.

Millions of women and old people no longer dare to go out onto the streets after dark.

Vandalism is commonplace in all our cities.

Why?

This book will tell you.

THE PURPOSE

The aim of this book is to help you find out how to enjoy life, regain your zest for living, banish mental tiredness, overcome loneliness, conquer stress and find lasting happiness in an increasingly cruel and crazy world.

This book is dedicated to the sensitive, the considerate and the caring; the victims of the Twentieth Century Blues.

TOXIC STRESS
AND
THE TWENTIETH CENTURY
BLUES

VERNON COLEMAN

CONTENTS

INTRODUCTION

My first book on stress was published back in 1978. It was called 'Stress Control' and at the time the word 'stress' was very new.

In the book I explained how stress – by which I meant pressure, worry and anxiety – could have an adverse effect on our mental and physical health.

The medical profession did not greet the book with any great enthusiasm. One professor of medicine publicly attacked me for suggesting that stress might be a contributory factor in the development of high blood pressure. Other eminent doctors dismissed the theory that stress could be responsible for the epidemic of mental illness as simplistic nonsense. I was attacked by doctors for suggesting that the widespread habit of over prescribing benzodiazepine tranquillisers would lead to the biggest addiction problem the world had ever seen.

But patients loved the book. Thousands of people bought it and, according to their letters, found it helpful. Eventually, doctors even started recommending the book to their patients – instead of handing them prescriptions for tranquillisers!

Throughout the eighties I wrote extensively about a wide range of medical subjects. But stress remained a popular subject with other authors. Hundreds of books were published and thousands of newspaper and magazine articles about stress appeared.

You might have thought that all these books and articles would have helped patients to control their stress effectively and permanently.

But despite all the attention the problem hasn't gone away.

Instead, it has got worse.

By the end of the 1980s the incidence of stress related disease had reached truly epidemic proportions and just about every doctor in the country was prepared to recognise the part stress plays in the development of disease.

Why, when so many people are aware of the damage that can be done by stress, has stress continued to do increasing amounts of damage?

There are two answers.

First, much of the stress to which we are exposed is outside our control. We have become increasingly aware of the ways in which our own behaviour can increase our exposure to stress and we have been taught many ways to reduce our vulnerability and to stress-proof our bodies. But this information is of limited value when it comes to dealing with general, social stresses – many of which are difficult to identify and impossible to avoid. I have coined the phrase 'toxic stress' to describe these insidious and destructive social stresses.

Second, we have failed in our attempts to control the damage done by stress because we have put all our effort into trying to find medical solutions. Hypnotherapists recommend hypnotherapy. Acupuncturists offer acupuncture as a solution. Herbalists recommend herbs and old fashioned, orthodox physicians prefer to prescribe drugs. All these remedies can be of value. But they work only by suppressing the symptoms of illness produced by stress. None of these techniques help to combat toxic stress.

Toxic stress is a result of social changes. And the only way to stay healthy and avoid the damage that can be done by toxic stress is to learn how to survive in the world we have created for ourselves.

Having studied the subject of stress for over twenty years I am convinced that many of the commonest symptoms and disorders seen today are caused not by individual stresses or pressures but by the high level of toxic stress that affects us all. I believe that toxic stress is responsible for producing a condition which is best described as The Twentieth Century Blues. My researches convince me that between one third and one half of the population in developed countries are already suffering from The Twentieth Century Blues – a serious condition which goes unrecognised by doctors and other healers. Furthermore I believe that the treatments usually prescribed for sufferers from The Twentieth Century Blues are frequently likely to cause more problems than they solve.

In this book I have, for the first time, explained the causes of toxic stress – and the solutions to The Twentieth Century Blues.

Vernon Coleman

Devon 1990

PART ONE

TOXIC STRESS AND THE TWENTIETH CENTURY BLUES

CHAPTER ONE

We live in strange, difficult and confusing times.

In some ways – largely material – we are richer than any of our ancestors.

In other ways – largely spiritual – we are infinitely poorer.

Most of us live in well equipped homes that our great grand parents would marvel at. We have access to (relatively) clean drinking water at the turn of a tap. We can obtain light to work by and heat to cook by at the flick of a switch. Our homes are stuffed with possessions. We have automatic ovens, washing machines, tumble driers, dish washers, food blenders, vacuum cleaners, television sets, video recorders and a whole host of other devices designed either to make our working hours easier or our leisure hours more enjoyable. If we want to travel anywhere we can climb into our own motor cars or we can use public buses, trains or aeroplanes. We have become so dependent upon these 'things' that when they break down we become aggressive and irritable. We can't cope without them.

We are surrounded by the gaudy signs of our wealth and the physical consequences of human ambition and endeavour, but loneliness, unhappiness, anxiety and depression now seem commoner than ever before in our history. There has never before been so much sadness, dissatisfaction and frustration as there is today. The demand for tranquillisers and sleeping tablets has risen steadily throughout the last few decades as our national and individual wealth has multiplied.

We have access to sophisticated communications systems and yet never before have we been so aware of our ignorance. We have more power over our environment than our ancestors ever dreamt of having and yet we are regularly reminded of our helplessness and our vulnerability. We are materially wealthy and yet spiritually deprived. We have conquered our planet and begun to conquer space and yet we are continually reminded of our woeful inability to live in peace with one another.

As our race becomes materially richer and more powerful so we as individuals seem to become spiritually poorer and more frightened. The more we acquire the more we seem to need and the more we learn the more we seem condemned by our ignorance. The more control we have over our environment the more damage we seem to do to ourselves. The more successful we become in financial terms the more we seem to destroy the qualities and virtues which lead to happiness and contentment. The more we learn about our world the more we seem to forget about our duties and responsibilities to one another.

As manufacturers and advertisers have deliberately translated our wants into needs so we have exchanged generosity and caring for greed and self concern. Politicians and teachers, scientists and parents have encouraged each succeeding generation to convert simple dreams and aspirations into fiery no-holds-barred ambitions. In the name of progress we have sacrificed common sense, goodwill and thoughtfulness and the gentle, the weak and the warm hearted have been trampled upon by hordes of embittered, miserable victims who have been taught only to think of the future and never to think of the present or the past. Our society is a sad one; the cornerstones of our world are selfishness, greed, anger and hatred. Those are the driving forces we are taught to respect.

During the last fifty years or so we have changed our world almost beyond recognition. Advertising agencies, television producers and newspaper editors have given us new aims to strive for, new hopes, new ambitions and new aspirations. At the same time they have also given us new fears and new anxieties. With the aid of psychologists clever advertising-copywriters have learned to exploit our weaknesses and our natural apprehensions to help create demands for new and increasingly expensive products. Our world has changed dramatically. Values and virtues have been turned upside down and inside out. Tradition, dignity and craftsmanship have been pushed aside in the search for ever greater productivity and profitability.

It is hardly surprising that all these changes have produced new stresses and strains of their own. The pressure to succeed joins with the pressure to conform and the pressure to acquire and as a result we live today in a world where the base levels of stress are fixed at dangerously high levels.

Each one of us is, of course, confronted with individual stresses on a daily basis. Everywhere you look you come face to face with individual and personal stresses. There are stresses in your business life and stresses in your social life. But these are stresses that you can easily do something about. You can choose to avoid them if you want to. You can confront them or control them. You can share them or simply deal with them yourself. You have some freedom of action because these are personal stresses.

The stresses which are an inherent part of the world around you – the world in which you and I and all of us must live – are quite different. These stresses – the ingredients of toxic stress – are not so easily avoidable. These stresses produce difficult to define frustrations. They produce bitterness and a deep sense of ill defined, unexplained despair.

The stresses created by advertisers and politicians, teachers and scientists, journalists and broadcasters are the stresses which, together, make up the unacceptable levels of toxic stress which are responsible for so much sadness, so much misery and so much despair. It is the existence of high levels of toxic stress which helps to explain why individual attempts to deal with stress have so often proved ineffective. It is the existence of toxic stress which explains why millions of people who believe that they have the stress in their lives under control are, nevertheless, suffering from stress related disorders.

CHAPTER TWO

Toxic stress is the commonest, most far reaching and most destructive force at work in our society today. It is far more invasive, more damaging and more universal than any infective organism.

Like personal stresses, toxic stress (which is primarily a social stress) can cause an enormous range of individual symptoms and well defined diseases. It can cause headaches, skin rashes and bowel disorders. It can cause asthma, high blood pressure, heart disease and peptic ulceration. It can cause sleeplessness, backache and hair loss. It can cause depression, psoriasis and sexual problems. It can make existing diseases worse and it can increase your susceptibility to infectious diseases, cancers and psychological problems.

But my researches over the last twenty years have also convinced me that toxic stress is responsible for something else; something specific and something that has never before been recognised as an individual syndrome. I have named the disease caused by toxic stress 'The Twentieth Century Blues'.

I believe that 'The Twentieth Century Blues' is almost certainly one of the commonest diseases in the developed world. I suspect that it is as common as tooth decay or the common cold. It is certainly far more damaging than any other common ailment.

The range of individuals suffering from this discomforting and incapacitating disease is vast. The executive or company director who works for a large company (and who seems, on the surface, to have more control over his environment than his employees) is as vulnerable to the effects of toxic stress as anyone else. The housewife, the student, the nurse and the doctor are all potential victims. The retired bank manager is as vulnerable as the young bank clerk and the junior shop assistant is as likely to suffer as the chairman of the store.

The only common factor is that victims of The Twentieth Century Blues tend to be sensitive, considerate and caring individuals. The more thoughtful and imaginative you are the more you are likely to become a victim and the more likely you are to suffer.

But not even the unintelligent and the uncaring are immune to the power of toxic stress. I believe that much modern hooliganism and vandalism (notably that associated with large crowds) is a result of toxic stress.

The sensitive and intelligent respond to toxic stress by becoming unhappy and confused. The insensitive and unintelligent respond to toxic stress by becoming angry, aggressive and violent. The deep sense of frustration commonly felt by the victims of toxic stress can lead one individual to withdraw and become more alone. The same feeling of frustration can lead another individual, with a different personality and living in a different environment, to become a dangerous sociopath.

CHAPTER THREE

Diagnosing 'The Twentieth Century Blues' is something that you have to do yourself – the disease has yet to be recognised by the medical establishment (and in view of the fact that the disease cannot be treated with any of the traditional remedies favoured by orthodox minded physicians I suspect that it will be some time yet before the disease is widely accepted within the medical profession).

To make it relatively easy for you to diagnose your condition I have listed below the symptoms which are associated with the syndrome. I have put the symptoms in question form and I want you to think carefully before answering them. Don't rush through answering them with a quick 'yes' or a quick 'no'. This is no ordinary quiz.

If you find that you can honestly answer 'yes' to one or more of these questions then you are, I suspect, one of the many victims of The Twentieth Century Blues. The more times you answered 'yes' the more serious your affliction.

If you discover that you are a toxic stress victim – and a sufferer of The Twentieth Century Blues – please do not despair. In the third part of this book I will explain to you how you can rebuild your strength and your resistance to toxic stress. The Twentieth Century Blues *can* be beaten.

Symptom one

Do you often feel that you ought to be doing more with your life? Do you feel dissatisfied with yourself or your life without really knowing why?

Symptom two

Do you have an uncomfortable – and difficult to explain – feeling that control of your life is slipping (or has slipped) away from you?

Symptom three

Do you suffer a lot from symptoms and ailments for which there never seems to be any completely satisfactory treatment? Do your symptoms or ailments hang on apparently endlessly – never really disappearing completely?

Symptom four

Do you often feel nervous or anxious even though you know that you don't really have anything to be nervous or anxious about?

Symptom five

Even though you may have a large family and lots of friends do you ever feel strangely and inexplicably alone?

Symptom six

Do you constantly feel rushed – unable to find the time to do all the things you feel you ought to do, let alone the things that you would like to do?

Symptom seven

Do you frequently worry unreasonably about quite trivial, insignificant things that in your heart you know don't really matter?

Symptom eight

Do you constantly feel tired, listless and short of energy – feelings for which there is no medical explanation?

Symptom nine

Do you ever feel an almost overwhelming and almost irresistible urge to run away from everything?

Symptom ten

Do you feel that life isn't as much fun as it used to be or should be? Do you go for whole days without ever really feeling happy or feeling glad to be alive?

Symptom eleven

Have you ever felt a frightening and unnerving urge to be violent – either to someone close to you or to some complete stranger who has annoyed you? Have you ever gone cold after realising how close you've been to initiating a frenzied physical attack on another human being?

Symptom twelve

Do you ever feel a complete sense of despair about the future of the world? Do you ever feel glad that you're not going to live to see the sort of world your children's children will inherit when they grow up?

CHAPTER FOUR

If you have decided that you are suffering from The Twentieth Century Blues please do not despair. You are by no means alone. At least one third of the people you know feel exactly the same way. Outwardly they may appear strong and happy but deep down inside they are just as tormented as you. You may find this difficult to believe but just remember that unless they know you very well they probably don't know that there is anything wrong with you either. You too have probably managed to put on a false front for several years now.

The difference between you is that you have now managed to find out what is wrong with you. And you can learn how to deal with the toxic stress which is causing your symptoms.

How can I describe the symptoms of The Twentieth Century Blues with such certainty?

That isn't difficult to answer.

Over the last twenty years I have received letters and telephone calls from hundreds of thousands of people who have described to me the symptoms which I now recognise as typical of The Twentieth Century Blues.

There is one final symptom which is almost universal among sufferers from this syndrome: guilt.

People who suffer from The Twentieth Century Blues invariably feel ashamed of the fact that they feel unhappy, frustrated, bored or discontent. They feel that since they enjoy much better living conditions than their ancestors – or, indeed, millions of people who are less fortunate than themselves – they ought to be grateful rather than dissatisfied. They feel guilty about the fact that they are miserable when their problems are trivial and superficial when compared to the problems endured by families living in under-developed countries.

This deep sense of guilt makes The Twentieth Century Blues more destructive, more damaging and even more unbearable.

CHAPTER FIVE

Why, if toxic stress and The Twentieth Century Blues are so common, have neither of them been recognised and written about by doctors before now?

It's a simple question.

And the answer is simple too.

Doctors are trained to look for physical causes for diseases – and to look for physical solutions too. Ever since the modern medical profession developed in the middle of the nineteenth century doctors have tried to find anatomical, physiological or biochemical explanations for all health problems.

It took years for doctors to accept that psychological pressures could cause any sort of illness and the general significance of stress was only fairly recently recognised by the profession as a whole.

It is not by accident that doctors are trained to try and cure illness by prescribing pills, performing surgery or intervening in some other essentially practical way. Doctors earn their living by providing practical services and the links between the medical profession and the powerful drugs industry (which, of course, makes its massive profits out of the drugs that doctors prescribe) are extremely close.

Indeed, the sad truth is that although doctors have not yet recognised the existence of toxic stress or The Twentieth Century Blues they have for several years now been attempting to treat the symptoms suffered by people who are toxic stress victims. And their attempts to treat such patients – usually by prescribing tranquillisers but sometimes by recommending electrical treatments or brain surgery – have frequently made things worse rather than better. Tranquillisers solve none of

13

the fears or anxieties caused by toxic stress and they cure none of the problems associated with The Twentieth Century Blues. Indeed, because they are frequently addictive and because the list of side effects associated with their use seems endless tranquillisers have created new problems.

The fact is that medical treatment isn't the answer to toxic stress or The Twentieth Century Blues because neither toxic stress nor the syndrome it produces are essentially medical problems. The word 'toxic' is used as a synonym for 'poison' and toxic stress is an insidious, morally and spiritually destructive disease. It eats away at the soul but it is not a disease that is ever likely to respond to a pharmacological therapy. The Twentieth Century Blues is a disease of the soul rather than the mind; a disorder of the spirit rather than the body. There is no chemical or biochemical abnormality associated with it.

For the same reasons the attempts by alternative practitioners to treat patients who are suffering from the effects of toxic stress have been similarly unsuccessful. During the last decade or two millions of patients have turned to alternative practitioners for help. They have done so partly because they have been disenchanted by orthodox medicine, partly because they have been alarmed by the quantity and severity of side effects associated with modern medical remedies and partly because they have found alternative practitioners to be, on the whole, more sympathetic, more understanding and less hurried than their more orthodox counterparts.

But alternative healers have also failed to identify the existence of toxic stress or The Twentieth Century Blues and although their remedies may sometimes be safer and gentler alternative practitioners still believe in the principles of interventionism. A study of the therapies recommended by alternative practitioners shows that they, like their orthodox colleagues, have made the mistake of trying to treat this problem, and the symptoms associated with it, as a *medical* problem. Some practitioners have gone so far as to define new syndromes in an attempt to explain away symptoms for which there is no convenient physical explanation. There has been much talk of allergies, hidden infections and ecological disasters. Inevitably, perhaps, new remedies have also been unearthed. I doubt if there is a mineral or a vitamin which has not, at one time or another, been recommended as a 'cure' to patients suffering from what I now believe to be The Twentieth Century Blues.

The alternative practitioners have failed and their remedies have proved ineffective because toxic stress cannot be treated as a medical problem and The Twentieth Century Blues cannot be cured with traditional interventionist therapies. There have been some short term successes, of course. And these temporary successes have helped to create new myths, new diseases and new 'wonder' cures. But these temporary successes have been a result of placebo power rather than anything else. Patients have got better because of the attention they have received rather than because of the pills they have been given. Patients have recovered because they have, to some extent, been shielded from the real world, and therefore from toxic stress.

The final and significant truth is that because toxic stress is a force which affects the soul and because The Twentieth Century Blues is an affliction of the spirit the answer must lie outside orthodox medical thinking.

PART TWO

THE CAUSES OF TOXIC STRESS

INTRODUCTION

When we are feeling angry or upset with the world we often blame 'them'.

When we feel that we are being forced to do things against our will we blame 'them'.

When we feel frustrated or cheated we blame 'them'.

When we are hampered by injustice or wounded by unfairness we say that it is 'their fault'.

But there is no 'them' of course.

The man who seems to represent injustice – and seems one minute to be one of 'them' – will, the next minute, be standing shoulder to shoulder with you sharing your complaints.

The opponents of justice and fair play have no human form.

The truth is that when we are complaining about 'them' we are really complaining about the world we have created for ourselves; we are complaining about the unseen forces which structure our society; we are complaining about things which are now out of our control.

The real problem is that we are no longer in true control of our destiny.

We have created a world, a society, which now exists to protect itself! We have created a society which exists to improve and strengthen itself at our expense. The real threat to our health comes not from the atomic bomb or the fact that we are steadily destroying our world but from the fact that we have created a social structure in which we now exist as mere pawns.

In the remainder of this section I will explain the ways in which toxic stress is created.

CHAPTER ONE

Our exposure to toxic stress begins at a very early age. It starts in earnest the moment we attend school for the first time.

We are all taught to take education seriously. We are told that our education will shape and govern our lives. We are told that if we work hard at school and at college then we will reap the benefits later.

What we are told is true.

But we are not told the price that we will have to pay for our years of education. We are never told the price that society expects us to pay in return for having our lives shaped and improved.

To understand the potential costs to your spirit and your soul you must first understand the *purpose* of the education society is offering you. You must understand what society stands to gain from the deal you are being offered. Sadly, nothing that society offers you ever comes free. An education is certainly no exception. The main reason society offers to educate you is to prepare you for work. Society doesn't want to educate you so that you become a more thoughtful, more creative or wiser person. What would be the point of that? Society doesn't want to broaden your horizons or enhance your sense of vision. Society doesn't want to instill passion in you (that can be troublesome and inconvenient) and it doesn't want you to know how to think for yourself (that can be costly and disruptive).

What society really wants is obedience.

Society – the social structure which we have created but which has now acquired a strength and a force of its own (inspired by its own need to survive) values obedience highly and rewards the obedient more than any other group. Society knows that the obedient will work hard without question. Society knows that the obedient can be relied upon to do work that is dull, repetitive and possibly even dangerous. Society knows that the obedient are unlikely to be troubled by spiritual or moral fears. Society knows that the obedient will fit neatly into whatever hierarchy may exist and society knows that the obedient will put loyalty above honesty and integrity. Society will always reward those who are obedient because that shows other people the value of obedience! If you become obedient then you will also become a good and reliable customer. You will buy things that you don't need and so help society to evolve and stay strong. You will accept shoddy workmanship and unreliability without complaint. You will accept new fashions as necessary and you will buy new clothes and new cars when society wants you to buy these things – not when you *need* them. The obedient customer is a passive customer and the passive customer is the best customer.

Think back to your own education and you'll see how important obedience was. Any course which involves a text-book and a teacher and concludes with an examination is designed to prevent thought and to encourage blind obedience. The educational system prepared you for a life in a meritocracy where nothing is more meritorious than silent obedience.

If you were a good student then you will have been rewarded.

If your education was successful – on society's terms – then you will have been offered choices that marked you for life. Whatever profession you chose to follow society will have taught you to feel special. You will have been encouraged to believe that you are superior to all those who do not have your own specific skills. You will have been taught to feel contempt for those who do not have your authority. You will have been taught prejudices rather than truths.

You must remember that the aim of a modern education is to harness the minds of the imaginative or potentially disruptive. Such individuals are dangerous to a smooth running society. Society's schoolteachers – the handmaidens of the system – are prepared and willing to manipulate the minds of the young because that is what society expects them to do in return for their own status in society. Everything is designed to help produce a neat and layered world.

The price you pay for your education is a high one. And the more successful your education is in society's terms (and the higher your position in the meritocracy) the greater the price you must pay. You will be marked for life. Your choices – or the choices that society helped you to make – will have strictly defined the boundaries of your life. You may be better rewarded (in material terms) than many of those who were less capable of satisfying the system but the price you pay will be higher too. The price you pay for educational success is intellectual constraint. You pay for your success with your freedom. You pay for your success with guilt, frustration, dissatisfaction and boredom.

The modern educational system is designed to support the structure of our society but it is also a major force in the development of toxic stress.

CHAPTER TWO

At about the same time that you entered the educational system you also became a consumer.

Whatever you choose to do with your life you will, to much of the world, always be a consumer.

People who make motor cars, bicycles, washing machines, television sets and microwave ovens think of the people who buy their products as *consumers* not *people*. Those who sell bread, milk, cheese, eggs and flour sell their produce to consumers. People who sell holidays, restaurant meals, hotel accommodation and train tickets aim their advertising at consumers. Accountants, lawyers, surveyors, doctors and agents of a hundred different types earn their living from consumers.

In order to persuade you to buy their products or services (and to spend ever increasing amounts of money on them) the people who make or sell these products or services will spend considerable amounts of money on trying to persuade you that the products or services they sell are better than anyone elses. Society needs them to do this in order to survive and, even more important, in order to expand and grow ever richer.

And so every day your custom will be solicited in a thousand different ways – some crude and some subtle. Every day you will come face to face with an almost infinite variety of messages and exhortations.

The professionals who prepare the advertisements with which you are confronted are only too aware of the fact that it is no longer enough for them to tell you of the value of the product that they are selling. These days the competition is so great that advertising agencies are no longer content to tell you how to satisfy your basic needs. These days advertising agencies know very well that in order to succeed in the modern market place they must create *new* needs; their advertising must create wants and desires, hopes and aspirations and then turn those wants, desires, hopes and aspirations into *needs*. They do this through exaggeration and deceit and through exploiting your weaknesses and your fears. They create layer after layer of toxic stress in order to turn you into an ever more eager customer.

Modern advertising agencies know (because they've done the necessary research) that it is impossible to sell anything to a satisfied man. But, in order to keep the wheels of industry turning, in order to keep the money coming in, in order to ensure that society continues to expand, the advertising agencies must keep encouraging us to buy; they must constantly find new and better ways to sell us stuff we don't want. Any fool can sell us products and services that we need. The trick is in turning our most ephemeral wants into basic needs. In order to do this advertising agencies must use all their professional skills to make us dissatisfied with what we already have. They need us to be constantly dissatisfied and frustrated. They constantly need to create new and more virulent forms of toxic stress.

Modern advertising raises the intensity of our desires and builds our dissatisfaction and our fears in order to satisfy its own mercenary ends. Modern advertising is a creative art. The advertising professional is hired to create unhappiness and dissatisfaction. He is paid to make us want more possessions, excitement or status. He is paid to keep us dissatisfied.

The advertising people will do their best to make you dissatisfied with anything which cannot be profitable for them. They want to take away your appreciation of the simple things in life so that they can sell you complicated and expensive things. They would rather you sat down to watch football on TV than that you kicked an old ball around in the park. They want you to wash away your natural, sexual odours and replace them with odours taken from the sexual glands of animals. They want you to be in so much of a hurry that you eat instant foods rather than growing and then preparing your own vegetables. They want you to ride in a car rather than walk or ride a bicycle. They want you to forget your needs and replace them with wants out of which they can make a profit. They want you to feel guilty if you don't smell right or don't look the way they want you to look. They want you to feel guilty if you don't buy the new season's clothes. They want you to feel a failure if you don't buy the latest toys or fill your house with the latest gadgets and bits and pieces of equipment.

They don't want you to be able to wear the clothes you like or feel comfortable in. They don't want you to be able to walk freely through our towns and cities. They don't want you to enjoy any *real* freedom. They need your money and so they want your soul.

Or maybe they just *need* your soul because they *want* your money.

The advertising industry is responsible for much of the sickness and much of the unhappiness in our society.

Even if you do buy the products they want to sell you, you will still not find the satisfaction they promise you. Their advertisements are shallow, their promises empty and hollow.

Their advertising may suggest that if you buy their product you will become popular and successful. The suggestion will be made with care and caution. The advertisers are subtle in their cruelty.

But you will be disappointed. Even if you buy the product you will remain frustrated and dissatisfied. The advertising professionals make many promises which they know they cannot keep.

To the spiritual and mental frustration created by all this disappointment you must add physical frustration too for the chances are high that the product you buy will soon fail. Obsolescence is built in and essential to all new products. Built in mechanical or fashionable obsolescence enables the car companies to keep making and selling us new cars (even though most of us already have cars which work perfectly well) and the manufacturers of television sets to keep making and selling new television sets.

Sadly, the advertising professionals don't care about the poor, the disabled and the sick or frail. Such people are not good consumers. Modern advertising destroys the poor. It shows them things they cannot have. It shows them services they cannot buy. It inflames their desires. It creates wants and then turns those wants into needs. It creates frustration. It creates passion. And it creates violence. The poor do not even have the simple satisfaction of discovering that the products they are offered are never likely to satisfy the promises made for them.

I believe that advertising is one of the greatest causes of toxic stress and is, therefore, one of the greatest of all modern threats to physical and mental health. Advertising agencies kill far more people than industries which pollute the atmosphere. Advertising is built on promises that can never be kept. Advertising is designed to replace your freedom with constraints. Advertising agencies succeed by making people unhappy. Advertising is the symbol of modern society; it represents false temptations, hollow hopes and unhappiness and disenchantment; it inspires values which are based on fear, greed and avarice.

CHAPTER THREE

Society's next great need is to convince you of the importance of progress.

Without progress society would stand still. Without progress industry would slow down. Without progress we would learn to enjoy our world and our lives. Without progress we would find happiness, contentment and stability more enjoyable than frustration. Without progress we would not know the meaning of dissatisfaction but society would not grow. Without progress the structure of our society would not increase in importance.

We have created a world and a society which now controls us. We' do not have power over our destiny but there are no people behind the scenes manipulating our lives. Our present and our future are controlled by the social structure we have devised. Our institutions and our establishments need progress in order to gain more power. We like to blame the invisible 'them' for our graceless state but there are no invisible 'them'. The men and women who have positions of authority in our society are as tortured by toxic stress as everyone else. They suffer as you and I do. The power is now vested in the institutions themselves; it is the structure which controls us.

And in order to grow the structure needs progress.

In order to help maintain and build the social structure which gives them their power and their authority the individuals who work for institutions and organisations and parts of the establishment readily insist that progress is vital. They know that without progress, without growing, *their* part of the social structure, and therefore *their* personal status, will decline. They know that in order to survive they must keep their institution alive and strong. And that means progress. The men and women who work for big companies know that without progress their companies will decline and lose power. The individuals who work for political institutions know that without progress and growth their status and power will decline. Everyone with an ounce of status or an ounce of power has a vested interest in progress.

And so everyone says what a good thing progress is and how impossible it is to halt progress. They tell us that progress is vital and good but they are lying. What they really mean is that progress is good for business or that progress offers some advantage in terms of money or power to the part of the social structure to which they are tied. Progress is, ironically, essential to the status quo.

Inevitably, anyone who works for any company or institution will insist that progress means 'better'. It doesn't. Progress means that people have to work harder and take life more seriously. Progress means that 'things' become more complicated and more likely to go wrong. Progress means that the 'things' you bought yesterday (and were happy with) are outdated and useless within months. Progress means that new is always better and that the future is always stronger than the past.

Progress means that more and more people have to exchange a rich, varied, wholesome, healthy lifestyle for one which is hollow and filled with despair and loneliness. Progress means deprivation for people but strength for our social structures. Progress means that the jobs people do become more boring and less satisfying. Progress means more power to machines. Progress means that things are more likely to go wrong. Progress means more destruction, more misery and more tedium. Progress means more damage to our planet. Progress means more toxic stress.

Those who worship at the altar of progress make two simple but vital errors. They assume that man must take full advantage of every new development and invention. And they assume that he must always search for a better way of tackling everything he does.

Neither of these two assumptions is soundly based.

Just because man invents computers, supersonic jets and atomic bombs he doesn't have to *use* these things.

Those who believe implicitly in progress believe that we must always endeavour to use every new nugget of information we obtain. They believe that if man invents a faster way to travel then the faster way to travel must be better than the old way. They believe that if man invents a quicker and more effective way to kill people then we must use this quicker and more effective weapon of destruction. They believe that if man invents a faster way to do mathematical equations then all our industries must be adapted to take advantage of this new technology.

These assumptions are not based on logic or fact.

Progress for the sake of progress often simply means change for the sake of change. Change is not always for the better.

Nor is there much sense in the belief that man must always busy himself looking for better ways to do things.

The problem lies largely with the definition of the word 'better'.

What, exactly, does it mean?

Is a television set *better* than a radio?

Is a motor car better than a bicycle?

Is an aeroplane better than a yacht?

Are modern motor cars, equipped with electric windows and air conditioning, better than ancient Rolls Royce motor cars equipped with neither of these facilities?

Is artificial turf better than real grass?

Are artificial flowers better than the real thing?

Too often progress simply means more frustration and more unhappiness. It means that we become more dependent on one another and less capable of coping with the crises in our lives.

Do people really get more pleasure out of cars which travel faster and look much the same as all the other models on sale?

Are people wiser, happier and more contented now that electric toothbrushes are available?

Are people more at peace than their ancestors now that the compact disc player has been invented and marketed?

How much did the telephone improve the quality of life?

The truth, of course, is something of a compromise. Some advances are good. Some new technology is helpful. Some new developments really do improve our lives. Some progress reduces pain and suffering.

But society isn't interested in the truth. And it certainly isn't interested in any compromise. Society needs uncontrolled progress in order to grow. Our society's institutions have an insatiable appetite for progress. And the people who acquire their power and their status and their wealth from those institutions do what they are expected to do. Our world is no longer controlled by people. It is controlled by the structure we created.

The truth is that progress can be a boon as well as a burden. It would be stupid to claim that all progress is bad. Progress is good when we use it rather than when we allow it to rule our lives.

The truth, as always, is wonderfully simple: progress is neither good nor bad unless we make it so.

But we no longer are allowed to choose between those aspects of progress which we think can be to our benefit and those which we suspect may be harmful.

Our society wants progress and that is what it gets.

CHAPTER FOUR

As we grow so we are taught to have respect for science and technology. We are taught that science and technology have all the answers to the problems of today and tomorrow. We are told that science can help mankind conquer the future and that technology can help man deal with the problems that have been created by the present and the past.

The truth is that they are wrong; sadly, woefully, ingloriously wrong. The truth is that science and technology are the cause of much of our toxic stress. The truth is that science and technology are now largely dedicated to solving problems *created* by science and technology.

Science may sometimes appear to be an unstoppable power; a supernatural tower of strength packed with an immeasurable kaleidoscope of force, energy and talent.

It is none of those things.

Science is no more than a tool and like any tool it can be a force for evil as readily as it can be a force for good.

It is science which has enabled us to destroy much of our world.

It was science which gave us the ability to conquer, control and exploit nature. It was science which gave us pollution. It was science which gave us concrete and high rise tower blocks and endless ribbons of motorway. It was science which gave us road traffic accidents and air crashes and a thousand different varieties of death and destruction. It was science which gave us nuclear power and the ability to destroy ourselves. It was science which gave us chemicals which blind and drugs which numb and destroy the brain. It was science which gave us addiction and the sad need to search for drugs with which to escape from our world. It was science which gave us food which tastes of nothing more than cardboard. It was science which gave us unemployment and which took away from millions the natural pride and pleasure and quiet satisfaction that can be obtained from a day's work well done. It was science which turned skilled craftsmen into miserable machine minders; removing pride, self expression and satisfaction from their lives.

Science created all these problems and worries and anxieties. And now science pushes us to search for new answers and solutions. And as it pushes so it creates new problems and new fears.

The truth, as always so clear, so simple and so undeniable, is that there are as many dishonest and deceitful scientists as there are honest and honourable scientists.

When we use science to help us live better, happier, cleaner, safer and more contented lives then science can be a powerful force for good. But too often science is an end in itself rather than a force for good. Too often science aids only scientists; too often science adds nothing to the quality of life.

Science and technology have contributed much to the existence of toxic stress in our world.

CHAPTER FIVE

Your ancestors lived in a world about which they understood very little. They should have been consumed by fear. Fear of the unknown. Fear of being eaten alive. Fear of starvation. Fear of death and illness.

We, by contrast, should lead relatively fear-free lives.

But all the evidence suggests that fear now plays a bigger part in our lives than it ever played in our ancestors lives.

Why?

Because our society needs us to be frightened.

Fear is a powerful driving force which helps to push us forwards. Fear encourages us to spend money, to accept progress and to treat those around us with contempt and disrespect. Fear helps to keep us weak but it helps to keep our society strong. Fear divides us and cripples us but gives our social structures strength. Today we are never allowed to forget our fears for an instant.

It is no accident that industries, advertising agencies, politicians, experts and television commentators all contribute to our daily ration of fear. There is nothing strange or inexplicable about the fact that one hardly ever sees or hears a pundit offering reassurance.

Fear is one of the most potent forces used to control us and to manipulate our emotions. It is fear which often leads us to change our habits – to the advantage of some part of our society. It is fear which justifies progress.

Take health, for example.

We are encouraged to worry about health in a million separate ways. Listen to the experts arguing about what is bad for you and you will soon feel twinges of fear nibbling at your increasingly tortured spirit.

Most of the time our fears are being manipulated by people – representing social structures – who want us to change our spending habits. We are told that we should eat less saturated fats and eat more products which contain unsaturated fats – by people who want to sell us unsaturated fats. We are encouraged to drink caffeine free coffee by people who want to sell us caffeine free coffee. We are encouraged to believe that smoking will help us by people who want to sell us cigarettes. We are encouraged to stop smoking by politicians who have been told that smoking damages industrial efficiency and costs society money.

We are encouraged to have regular health checks by doctors who want to charge us fees for the service they will gladly provide. We are encouraged to distrust doctors by people who want to sell us herbal medicines. We are encouraged to use sugar substitutes by companies making sweeteners. We are advised to avoid sweeteners by people selling sugar. We are told to eat more bran by people selling bran rich products. We are told to exercise by companies selling exercise equipment. We are told that cycling is dangerous by people who want us to buy their motor cars. We are told to put our faith in acupuncture, osteopathy, aromatherapy or psychotherapy. We are advised to take aspirin, vitamins, minerals or protein tablets. We are told to eat more runner beans, more carrots or more apples.

It is any wonder that we suffer from fear? Is it any wonder that hypochondriasis is commonplace? Is it any wonder that we suffer from toxic stress?

Fear is everywhere and is constantly used by people who want our support.

Politicians make us frightened of street violence in order to encourage us to allow them (and the social structures for which they work) to have more power. Police chiefs recommend stronger policing. Prison officers recommend better prisons.

Politicians make us frightened of our enemies abroad (even if our enemies abroad are no real threat to us) because by making us frightened they can win more power for themselves.

Fear is a potent weapon these days because the availability

of television and radio mean that we can be frightened more speedily and more effectively than ever before.

Every representative of every social structure uses fear to manipulate us. Fear helps our society to sustain itself and to increase its power.

No one seems to care about the damage done by the toxic stress that all this fear generates.

CHAPTER SIX

Much unhappiness and frustration is caused by the fact that in our society the law is commonly confused with justice, liberty, freedom and equality.

In truth the law has very little to do with these fundamental moral principles. The law exists to help society defend itself; it is used by those who represent society as a weapon with which to dominate and discriminate against individual powers and freedoms. The law is man's inadequate attempt to turn justice – a theoretical concept – into practical reality. Sadly, it is invariably inspired more by the prejudices and self interest of the lawmakers than by respect or concern for the rights of innocent individuals.

These misconceptions about the purpose of our law lead to much disappointment. And these misconceptions help to create a considerable amount of underlying toxic stress.

No society has ever had as many laws as we have. And yet few societies have had less justice.

Many of the laws which exist today were created not to protect individuals or communities but to protect the system. It is because such crimes threaten the security and sanctity of the system that theft and fraud often attract harsher sentences than crimes such as rape and murder which affect individuals – and (in society's terms) their less significant rights.

The irony is that although the law was originally introduced to protect individuals the law has itself become a tyrant. Today few individuals can afford to take advantage of the protection offered by the law. The law oppresses the weak, the poor and the powerless and sustains itself and the powers which preserve it. The cost of litigation means that there is one law for the rich and no law for the poor. The result is that the law threatens and reduces the rights of the weak and strengthens and augments the rights of the powerful.

Things are made worse by the fact that the people employed by society to uphold and administer the law on behalf of the ordinary people too often take advantage of their positions to abuse their powers. The interpretation of the law is so often at the discretion of those who are paid to uphold it that those who have been hired by society become the law itself: neatly and effectively society protects itself against any threat.

Too often society allows officers of the courts to abuse their power to satisfy their own personal prejudices, grievances and ambitions. In return society – and the structure which supports it – is protected by the people who benefit from its patronage. It is the worst sort of symbiotic relationship.

The final irony is that as respect for the law (and those hired to uphold it) diminishes so the divide between the law and justice grows ever wider.

When people who are given the power to protect society disapprove of something which threatens their status they introduce a new law. As political parties come and go so we accumulate layer after layer of new laws. It doesn't matter if the new laws conflict with the old laws as long as all the laws help to strengthen the status of the state.

Meanwhile as the oppression of individuals continues, lawlessness (and disrespect for the law) grows among officials and those in power. Brutality, arrogance, corruption and hypocrisy have all damaged public faith in the law but the only response from society has been to create new laws to outlaw disapproval. Society's primary interest is to protect itself and society is not concerned with justice, freedom or equality since those are values which are appreciated only by individuals. Society is concerned with progress and power and its own survival.

PART THREE

THE CURE FOR THE TWENTIETH CENTURY BLUES

INTRODUCTION

There are two ways to deal with any problem that affects
your health.

The simple, traditional way that has been preferred by
healers for centuries is to treat the symptoms of the disorder.

But the more sensible (and, in the long term, more efficient)
method is to tackle the cause of the symptoms.

If you've been electrocuted and your doctor attempts to
treat your symptoms without removing you from the live electrical supply then all his work will be in vain. If you are drown-
ing then there isn't much point in performing artificial
respiration until you've been dragged out of the water.

The symptoms associated with The Twentieth Century
Blues vary enormously from one sufferer to another. One individual may have the symptoms of irritable bowel syndrome.
Another may suffer from panic attacks. A third may suffer
from attacks of wheezing. Headaches, skin rashes and indiges-
tion are all extremely common.

Your doctor (or alternative healer) may be able to help
you control the symptoms that have been caused by The Twentieth Century Blues but the only way to deal with your problem
effectively and permanently is to tackle your susceptibility
to toxic stress.

And since toxic stress is a social rather than a medical
phenomenon your doctor or alternative therapist will almost
certainly be unable to help you to do that.

Because The Twentieth Century Blues is basically a disease
of the spirit the solutions are spiritual rather than physical.
You need to change long established attitudes and acquire
new understandings of yourself and the world in which you

live – rather than simply take pills or perform exercises.

In this final part of this book I'm going to show you exactly what you need to do to conquer the symptoms which are associated with The Twentieth Century Blues. I'm going to show you how to overcome your lethargy, how to conquer your deep seated anxieties and how to put some meaning and some joy back into your life. I believe that I can help you feel optimistic about the future.

Obviously, a book alone can't change your life for you. You have to be prepared to make some changes in the way you live and the way you think about the world. But if you are prepared to make the necessary adjustments and adaptations to your life then you will be able to deal with toxic stress and conquer TheTwentieth Century Blues.

CHAPTER ONE

When we are young we all have many dreams. We fantasise a lot about the future. We see ourselves becoming great painters, writers or sculptors. We envisage ourselves conquering the world as musicians, politicians or sports stars.

Gradually, as we get older, so our dreams are taken away from us.

People tell us that we must stop our day dreaming. They insist that we forget our fantasies, put aside our hopes and grow up into sensible,responsible, prosaic adulthood.

Society doesn't like dreamers. Society wants us to adopt a practical role. Society doesn't want people with their own visions for the future. Society likes us all to replace our personal visions for the future with simpler aspirations. Society wants us to put aside our dreams and forget all thoughts of romance and adventure. Society wants us to sell our souls for a small suburban house, a motor car and a barbecue in the garden.

Society needs workers and consumers not dreamers.

Society tells us all that dreams are for children and society (in the person of school-teachers, parents and employers) tells us that as we grow older so we must settle for more modest, more practical hopes.

But the rewards society offers us in exchange for our dreams are trivial and tarnish quickly. The irony is that the rewards society offers are a sham; they will crumble in your fingers. Only dreams are real.

The truth is that to succeed, to survive and to be happy you must always hold your dreams close to your heart. Never let them go. The people who escape from their surroundings are the people who can dream. The prisoners who survive concentration camps are the ones who can envisage a world after imprisonment. It doesn't matter what sort of world it is as long as it is a better world.

Ignore and resist the people who want to take away your dreams, ambitions and aspirations and who want to replace your dreams with ordinary satisfactions. Resist the pressure from those who want you to become a neat, productive human unit.

Keep your dreams close to you for as long as you live. Never let them go.

If your dreams are now but a distant part of your past rescue them. Reach back into your memory and grab them. Try to remember what your dreams were when you were a teenager.

If you allow your dreams to disappear then you will become sad, dull, aimless and miserable. Your life will have no romance. You will be deprived of the sort of hope and vision with which you can combat misery, pain and depression.

However old you are, however long you live, never allow yourself to be parted from the dreams, ambitions and hopes you enjoyed when you were a child. And don't be afraid to give your dreams substance and strength. Programme your dreams into your plans for your future.

When the boss of a large Japanese company was asked if his company had any long term goals he answered 'yes'.

'How far ahead do you plan?' asked the questioner.

'Two hundred and fifty years,' answered the Japanese businessman.

'What qualities do you need to carry out such long term plans?' asked the startled questioner, more accustomed to two or maybe five year plans.

'Patience!' replied the Japanese businessman.

Remember that a goal is nothing more than a dream with a deadline. Write your dreams down. Vow today that you will do something to turn them into reality.

Coleman's Law

You don't have to realise your dreams to benefit from them. But you do have to keep them alive.

CHAPTER TWO

Most people spend much of their lives striving to make money – and get rich.

It is a driving force which leads to much corruption, dishonesty, disappointment and unhappiness.

Many people die getting rich.

Some go to prison.

Some ruin relationships, lose friends and damage their health permanently.

But why do people want to get rich?

A few years ago a man who made a fortune out of other people's greed for money used the slogan: 'Do you sincerely want to be rich?'

As the man had expected most people who were asked the question answered 'Yes'.

And then he had them. And by offering them wealth as a reward he was able to get them to do things that were silly, illegal or both.

He got rich, they got poor.

I want to ask you a different question.

'Do you sincerely *need* to be rich?'

Now what's your answer?

Coleman's Law

More people are made miserable trying to get rich – and failing – than are made happy by trying to get rich – and succeeding.

CHAPTER THREE

A friend of mine lives in a small but smart detached house in the suburbs. He has a wife, three children and two motor cars. He leaves home at 7 o'clock every morning and gets home at 9 o'clock at night. At the weekends he brings work home with him.

I visited him recently one Sunday afternoon and found him busy tinkering with a huge power mower that wouldn't start.

'Damned thing always takes an hour to start,' said my friend, throwing down a spanner disgustedly.

I looked around at his lawn. It was very small. It would have taken much less than an hour to cut it with a simple hand propelled mower.

'Do you need that great big thing?' I asked him.

He looked at me as if I had gone mad. 'No one round here cuts their grass by hand !' he said.

When we went into the house we had to squeeze past a static bicycle – one of those exercise machines that executives use to keep themselves healthy.

'How long have you had this?' I asked him.

'Just over a month,' said my friend. 'We used to keep it in the bedroom but whenever I used it the whole house shook and the downstairs ceiling started to crack.'

'Isn't it boring?' I asked him. 'Riding a bicycle in your own hallway?'

My fiend shrugged. 'I need the exercise,' he said. 'I spend three hours a day sitting in the car in traffic jams. I don't get time to go to the gym.'

'Three hours!' I said, surprised. 'An hour and a half each way?'

My friend nodded.

'But its only fifteen miles!'

'Twelve,' said my friend. 'The traffic is terrible.'

'You could get there quicker on a bike!' I said.

'Go to work on a bike!' said my friend, shocked. 'You must be joking. What would the neighbours say?'

*   *   *

My friend works long hard hours at a job he doesn't particularly enjoy to earn money to pay for two cars, a power mower and an exercise bike.

If he sold the power mower, the exercise bike and one of the cars and bought an ordinary bicycle and a push mower he'd get all the exercise he needed, save himself money and have far more time to spend with his family.

He might even be able to give up the job he doesn't like and find one (paying less money) that he found more satisfying.

But I don't think my friend will sell his power mower or his exercise bike.

He's been trapped by society's lunatic values. He's been trapped by the need to compete with his neighbours. (One of society's cleverest tricks). And, most of all, he's been trapped by his own vanity.

Look at your life. Do you lead a 'power mower and exercise bike' life?

If so then ask yourself who you're trying to impress. And whether or not you really care about what strangers think about you.

Coleman's Law

No one needs a power mower and an exercise bicycle.

CHAPTER FOUR

Society doesn't like you sitting down looking at the flowers.

While you're sitting down looking at the flowers you aren't consuming anything.

And when you aren't consuming industry, shop and banks aren't making a profit.

Banks and businesses desperately need you to go through life on the run. They need you to spend, to travel, to throw away and to replace. They need you to follow fashion. Money keeps the world turning and so society needs you to be greedy and ambitious.

If you sit down and watch the world go by then you are worthless to the social structure we have created. Every moment you spend lazily watching the clouds drift by, or watching birds and animals at play, or staring into the sunset, is a wasted moment as far as society is concerned.

All this explains why you feel guilty if you stop and do nothing; why you feel guilty if you lie in bed on a Sunday morning or if you sit down when you could be doing something 'useful'.

Society knows that if you are to continue earning and spending then you must keep working. Society knows that if you're sitting around enjoying the world then you are unlikely to be consuming. And as far as society is concerned if you aren't consuming then you aren't real. As far as society is concerned a moment of contemplation is a moment wasted.

I suggest that you ignore society's demands and choose to take life at your own pace. Stop, sit, relax, and rest when you want to stop, sit, relax and rest.

Remember that time is the most precious commodity in

the world. No one knows how much any one of us has. And it is up to you to decide whether you want to waste or enjoy the hours you have left.

Remember that one commodity that is more precious than money is time.

Coleman's Law

Everyone knows that you can buy money with your time. But only the wisest realise that you can also buy time with your money.

CHAPTER FIVE

Nurture and take good care of real friendships. Friends are more valuable than any precious metal.

As the years go by you will meet many, many people. Some of them you will think of as no more than vague acquaintances. Many you will think of and refer to as friends.

But you will make very few *real* friends. You will not make real friends quickly or easily. Such relationships take many months, even years, to develop fully. But real friendships will last you a lifetime and provide you with support, succour and encouragement at the times of your life when you feel most lonely and vulnerable.

You will know when a real friendship develops.

When a real friend rings you for help you will stop what you are doing without thinking about the consequences. You will be prepared to go anywhere, do anything to help him or her. When a real friend rings you at three in the morning you will get out of bed and drive a hundred miles without wondering why or asking yourself why you are doing such an odd thing.

Real friendship is strong and can survive a thousand assaults. Real friendship is closer to true love than anything else you will ever experience.

Modern cities and apartment buildings can be savage, lonely places. Too often you will find the world to be cruel, harsh and unforgiving. But once you have acquired a true friendship you will never again fear loneliness, failure or poverty. You will face illness with strength and you will be able to confront adversity with hope. Friendship can provide you with a vaccination against unhappiness. When you have friends you can carry true love and affection and caring with you. Friendship will illuminate the darkest moments of your life and brighten the blackest of nights.

You will not make true friendships easily or quickly. Such friendships only develop with time and patience. But once you have found a real friend cherish him or her and always keep for him or her a place in your heart where your friendship can constantly rebuild its strength.

Coleman's Law

Real wealth is measured in friendships not in material possessions.

CHAPTER SIX

Always do work that you can be proud of and always take pride in the work that you do.

If bread is the staff of life then work is the rock upon which a healthy mind is built. Work is the central foundation upon which you can build a happy, contented and satisfying life.

You will find that many people around you do work which they hate and despise. They do their work purely for financial reward but because they have no pride in what they do their days are pointless, empty and quite meaningless.

Too many people are imprisoned by what they do; they do not exist outside their work and yet their work removes the soul from their spirit and leaves them cold, dull and lifeless. Millions move aimlessly through their days with only broken hopes and vanishing dreams to help sustain them through a constant stream of frustrations and disappointments. Millions are inspired by bitterness and envy rather than hope or joyful ambition. Millions spend their lives walking along windowless, endless corridors that take them from birth to retirement to death and never allow them to taste the pleasures of achievement or the inspiration of attainment.

A century ago the working man laboured long, hard and honestly to earn money to buy bread, coal and other essentials. Today the working man labours long and hard in order to satisfy his created wants rather than his basic needs. Today the working man spends his days creating worthless objects which he knows in his heart are valueless but which he knows he will be persuaded to buy. Today the working man works hard not because he needs the money he earns but because he thinks he needs the things that money will buy.

Look around you and you will see men and women selling their lives so that they can buy possessions they have been encouraged to covet. You will see men and women squabbling, moaning and whining as they work. You will see men and women working as little as they have to. You will see men and women doing work they are ashamed of and you will see men and women who hold themselves, and their own work, in contempt. You will see men and women who are not interested in making *good* products or offering a *good* service. You will see men and women who gain nothing and give nothing from their labours.

You will see millions of men and women who have prostituted their minds and their bodies to pay for badly made goods made by others who have prostituted their minds and their bodies to make them.

Look around and you will see that not even men and women who have creative jobs are above all this. You will see architects who design buildings in which they would not dream of living. You will see writers producing articles and books praising products and people who do not deserve their praise. You will see film directors selling their talents to those who want to sell their worthless products and their dubious services. Time and time again you will see artists selling their skills,their spirits, their pride and their integrity for a handful of silver.

Look around and you will see broken hopes, lost dreams and engrained bitterness. Look around and you will see people living their lives through others; you will see people who live through their television sets or through the imagined and exaggerated exploits of their heroes. Look around and you will see faces that show fear, obedience, hidden anger and uncertainty. You will see eyes that are hollow, dull and empty of every valuable human emotion. Look around and you will see people making products which they know to be either useless or harmful. You will see people maintaining bureaucratic structures which exist only to defend their own existence.

Always remember that what you do and how you do it is more important than your job title, what you earn or your position in the hierarchy.

A man may call himself a lawyer but if he spends all day

in dull offices making money out of creating unhappiness and maintaining the indecencies of the system then he has little cause for true pride.

A policeman who spends the day beating young demonstrators over the head with his truncheon may claim that he is helping to preserve society but no high flown phrase can disguise the fact that he has spent his day beating young people over the head with a truncheon.

An advertising copywriter may drive an expensive motor car and wear expensive clothes but if he spends his days writing lies and creating deceitful campaigns designed to create greed and need he has little cause for self satisfaction.

Always remember that success and profits never excuse hurtful or destructive behaviour. Remember that it is too easy to claim that the end will justify the means. Remember that it is no excuse to say that someone has to do it. 'If it wasn't me it would be someone else' is no excuse for a man or a woman who wants to live and die proud.

Look around you and you will see men and women working not with machines but for them. You will see men and women who have allowed machines to become superior to them.

Look around and you will see men and women who have dedicated their lives to jobs which they clearly find neither satisfying nor worthwhile.

Look around and you will see men and women who smile only when their work is over.

Try to be different. Try to remain always true to yourself. Always retain pride in what you do. Try to remain self sufficient. Earn what you need but never by selling your soul or your spirit. Sell your body before you sell your mind or your integrity.

Remember that the gardener may not earn as much as the insurance executive but he may be infinitely richer.

Run your life with pride. Do nothing that you regard as degrading or worthless.

Coleman's Law

It doesn't matter what you do for a living. What matters is how proud you are of what you do.

CHAPTER SEVEN

The modern world is full of cruel ironies and strange paradoxes.

One of the cruellest of all ironies is the fact that although we are living in a time when information systems are better than ever before communications between people are poorer than they have ever been. Too many people just don't say – or hear – the things which need to be said and heard.

Modern communications systems are sophisticated, fast, effective and powerful. Telephones, radios, fax machines and televisions have all revolutionised the art of communications. Our ancestors could speak to hundreds or shout to thousands. Today it is easy to speak to millions. Our ancestors were limited by the power of their voices. But today it is possible to reach a worldwide audience within seconds. News that would have taken years to spread from continent to continent can be around the world in an instant. Just a few years ago you needed to be standing next to someone to talk to them. Today you can stand in the middle of a field on one side of the world and speak to someone standing in a field on the other side of the world.

We live in the middle of a technological revolution. Communications technology has helped to shrink the world and the universe.

But the irony is that modern communications systems *add* to the toxic stress in your life!

Television programmes, newspapers, magazines and radio programmes enable us to hear bad news from around the world within seconds. There is always bad new somewhere. And so we are always being saddened, frightened and worried by some new disaster. We worry about earthquakes in America and about famine in Africa. We worry about floods in Asia and revolutions in Eastern Europe. We hear about financial crises in Argentina and we share the anguish of relatives when aeroplanes crash on the other side of the world.

But although the *science* of communication is undoubtedly more advanced than ever before the *art* of communicating is dying.

The science of communication has enabled us to share the worlds's worries but our ability to talk to one another and to share our own burdens with those around us has started to disappear.

The toxic stress in your life is infinitely more damaging than it should be because you don't talk to people as much as you should. And you probably don't listen enough either.

The irony is cruel.

We have better communications systems than our ancestors could have ever imagined. But we don't talk to one another. We can send messages around the world in seconds. We can bounce signals off satellites. We can fire information deep into space.But we don't talk to the people we love.

Look around. You will see that your neighbours and your friends hardly ever really talk to one another.They share gossip gleaned from the television set. They talk about fashions and celebrities.They talk about disasters and they moan together but they do not talk enough about how they feel.

We are almost drowned in information. Escape is impossible. Information pours out of our television sets and our radios. Messages come in every conceivable form.

But we seem to have been numbed by the eternal onslaught. The words that really matter are hardly ever spoken. People don't *talk* to one another. They don't share their personal agonies. They don't share their love, their pride or their hopes. Too often these things are seen as weaknesses.

And when the words are spoken they are rarely heard. The medium has suffocated the message.

And yet if you do talk to people you will benefit in a million different ways. Your relationships with those whom you love will grow even closer. You will understand the needs and hopes and fears of the people who are close to you and the people you work with. Problems and hazards will be avoided if only you will learn to talk.

Share your feelings with people and your relationships will flourish. If you love someone then tell him. If you are angry with someone then tell them. If you have something that must be said then say it. All around you people spend much of their lives swamped by the output of communications technology but very little time communicating with one another. People ring one another up and send one another memos but they do not share their feelings.

Learn to listen and you will benefit even more. Talking is a dying art but listening is almost dead. That's a tragedy. You can tell a great deal about someone by listening to what he has to say and the way he says it. Once you know a man's view on any major topic – whether it be the environment, the police, capital punishment or freedom of speech – you will know a good deal about the way he thinks and you will be able to predict and understand his other thoughts and his actions too.

Coleman's Law

Listening and talking are still the two most potent ways to communicate with other people.

CHAPTER EIGHT

Learn as much as you can about yourself. Learn about your strengths and your weaknesses. Learn about your good points and your bad points. Learn about your ambitions, your needs, your likes and your dislikes; learn how impulsive you are, how daring you are, how responsible you are, how optimistic you are and how practical you are.

Every relationship you have will involve an inter-reaction between two personalities. The more you know about yourself the more you will be able to understand why things sometimes go wrong. The more you understand your own needs and priorities the more you will be able to understand how best to work with other people.

If you don't know yourself then you'll never really get to know other people. If you don't understand yourself then you will never be able to recognise your limitations or your capabilities.

Regularly ask yourself how others see you. Ask yourself what sort of person you are.

Remember that we all behave differently in different situations, in different circumstances and with different people. You will be different when you're with those whom you love and trust to the way you are when you're with people who frighten you.

Try to comprehend the many facets of your personality; the many aspects of yourself that other see.

Finally, to find out your greatest weaknesses try to decide what you dislike most about other people.

The trait you find most horrendous in others is others is probably your own most dominant trait. If you can identify the things which annoy you most when exhibited by others then you will probably have identified the most significant aspects of your own personality.

Coleman's Law

The more you know about yourself the stronger you will become.

CHAPTER NINE

Once upon a time there were two bricklayers. They both did exactly the same work for the same local builder.

The first bricklayer found his work extremely tedious.

'All I do all day is lay one brick on top of another,' he complained. 'I get to work at 8.30 in the morning and lay bricks until its time for lunch. Then, after lunch, I lay bricks until it is time to go home. My only brief moment of satisfaction comes when I pick up my wage packet on a Friday afternoon.'

This bricklayer was away from work for several days every month – usually complaining of aching muscles, vague headaches and backaches. His real trouble was that he had no enthusiasm for his work. Whenever there was an excuse to stop what he was doing he would be the first man to lay down his trowel.

The second bricklayer enjoyed his work.

'I build houses,' he said proudly. 'Every day I think of the people who will occupy the house I am building. I think of their joy when they first see their new home. I think of the family that will grow up in it. I think of the generations who will decorate it and think of it as 'home'. I don't think of myself as building a wall or even a house. I'm building someone a *home*.'

This bricklayer – who had real purpose in his life – worked hard and worked well. He was hardly ever away from work. His colleagues and employers appreciated his enthusiasm and his love for his work.

The moral in this short anecdote is very simple: if you are to enjoy your life you need to have a purpose. Having a purpose will give you something to work for, something to look forward to and something to help you through the darkest of dark days. Without purpose any life will be hollow and unrewarding. With purpose and hope you will be able to survive everything fate can throw at you.

Once you have a purpose in your life you will be inspired by ambition and hope.

Without purpose your life will be sterile, empty and pointless. Having a purpose in your life will give you the power to combat the stresses and strains which are a consequence of boredom, pressures and frustrations.

Whatever job you choose, however old you are, whatever your personal responsibilities may be, your life needs purpose and direction as much as it needs food and oxygen. You need to be stretched, you need to take chances and you need to know that your life has been worthwhile.

Coleman's Law

The more purpose your life has the stronger you will be.

CHAPTER TEN

Never be afraid to speak your mind. You have nothing to lose but your chains.

You will meet many people – particularly those who work for large organisations – who are frightened to do or say anything that will annoy those who seem to have power.

You will find that the people who are most afraid to speak out are the people who have acquired some small status and position of their own – managers, civil servants and so on.

Such individuals are often afraid to speak out lest they lose their hard won power and authority. They are afraid to be honest in case they annoy those above them. They are afraid to make decisions and afraid to take risks.

Remember that people who never take risks never really succeed.

Remember that people who are not honest to themselves have nothing to be proud of.

And remember that the saddest person in the world is the individual who spends the final years of his life wondering what would have happened if he had had the courage to speak his mind and take a chance . . .

Coleman's Law

If you don't take chances you'll never know what would have happened. And you'll always wonder . . . and always regret.

CHAPTER ELEVEN

Because of the way our society is structured we are encouraged to have the greatest respect for the individual who has wealth.

To society this is important.

It means that the wealthy are rewarded while the poor are given an extra incentive to become rich.

But you should not fall into the trap of judging people by the clothes they wear, the cars they drive or the money they earn or have in the bank. Don't allow yourself to be misled into thinking that an advertising copywriter who drives an expensive sports car and wears designer suits is a *better* person than a farm labourer who rides a bicycle and wears tattered trousers and an old jacket.

Always try to deal with people as individuals, rather than as members of a category.

A doctor is no better or more important than a nurse. An administrator is no better or more important a person than a clerk.

Too often you will find that the people around you will allow a man's job or status to determine his worth in other aspects of his life.

But such judgements are nonsensical.

Financial success often depends more on fortune than talent. A lucky venture, a lucky investment, a lucky interview – all can lead to unexpected wealth.

Each social hierarchy is built on prejudice and chance.

An evil man can create a fortune for himself by making a product which ruins the environment or developing a process which exploits the innocent and the weak.

An honest, good and honourable man may be bankrupted

by chance.

Never judge a man or woman by the work they do (or do not do) and take care never to judge a man or woman until you know them as people.

A man who inherits money is no better (and no worse) than a man who wins money. Neither are intrinsically better or worse than the man who has earned his own money. And neither are better (or worse) than the man who has no money.

Coleman's Law

Judge people by who they are not what they own.

CHAPTER TWELVE

As well as having the courage to take chances – when the people around you are probably telling you not to – you should also try to find the courage to say 'no' when everyone else wants you to say 'yes'.

'No' is one of the shortest and one of the most difficult words to say in any language.

We all like to be liked and the easy way to be like is to say 'yes'.

When you say 'no' you inevitably disappoint the people who want you to say 'yes'. When you say 'no' you risk annoying acquaintances. The social pressure to say 'yes' can often seem overwhelming.

But if you don't say 'no' when you *want* to say 'no' you can lead yourself into all sorts of difficult and painful circumstances. Not having the courage to say 'no' can lead to commitments you can't cope with and to private, public and commercial engagements which you find at best dull and at worst difficult and painful.

Saying 'yes' when you really want to say 'no' can lead to all sorts of problems. And can hurt the people who are closest to you.

You will be tempted to say 'yes' because you have been put under pressure – maybe even blackmailed. You will be tempted to say 'yes' when you want to appear strong and decisive. You will be tempted to say 'yes' when you are frightened of what people might say or think if you say 'no'. You will be tempted to say 'yes' when you want to please the person who wants you to say 'yes'. You will be tempted to say 'yes' because other people have said 'yes'.

Remember: there is nothing wrong with saying 'no' occasionally. Remember that saying 'no' is almost always a sign of strength. Remember that having the courage to say 'no' is often a sign of maturity and self confidence.

Coleman's Law

When you have difficulty saying 'no' think of how much more difficult things are likely to become if you say 'yes'.

CHAPTER THIRTEEN

Your body is beautifully designed and built to last. It can withstand a wide range of pressures and cope with an enormous number of environmental hazards.

But occasionally things will go wrong. Being only human your body is vulnerable.

You will be encouraged to believe that whenever you are ill you should seek help from an expert. You'll find that professional help is available not just from doctors but also from a wide range of alternative or complementary practitioners. The demand for health care has risen so rapidly in the last few years that a huge new industry has developed. You'll find that there are hundreds of people prepared to tell you what to do in order to get well again. Inevitably, most of them will want to sell you their services or the products they manufacture or recommend.

Don't allow yourself to be tricked into believing that these health care experts have all the answers. They don't.

Privately most will admit that nine out of ten people who are ill will get better by themselves – without any complicated or expensive treatment or advice.

Sometimes you *will* need professional help, of course. The experts can occasionally save lives, obliterate pain and attack disease efficiently and effectively.

But often, I'm afraid, they do more harm than good.

Today doctors and other health care professionals are responsible for a horrifying amount of illness. They admit that when a patient has to be admitted to hospital there is a one in ten chance that he needs help because he has been made ill by a doctor. Doctors also admit that if a patient who is receiving treatment for one condition develops a second set of symptoms the chances are that the new symptoms were caused by the treatment for the original problem.

The real sadness is that many of the people who are injured by doctors never needed medical treatment in the first place. They went to see a doctor because they had been taught that when they were sick they always needed to ask for professional advice. They didn't know just how often they could manage without outside interference.

So learn to understand your body; learn to appreciate your own self healing skills; learn to acknowledge your body's miraculous range of techniques for dealing with threats and diseases.

The big trouble with most health care professionals – and this includes acupuncturists, osteopaths, aromatherapists and all the other 'alternative' practitioners as well as orthodox doctors – is that they treat their patients as battlegrounds, the illness as an enemy and their own armoury of drugs or techniques as weapons with which to fight the illness.

The reason for this is devastatingly simple. Whether he sticks needles into you, gives you herbal tea to drink or prescribes a drug for you to swallow the therapist has to do something to you or give you something to take in order to justify his fee.

The evidence to show that this interventionist philosophy is wrong is incontrovertible. When you fall ill you do not necessarily need to have anything done to you. Your body is equipped with such an enormous range of subtle and sophisticated feedback mechanisms that it can look after itself very well. Your body can heal itself, protect itself and guard itself against a thousand different types of threat. Your body contains internal mechanisms designed to enable you to deal automatically with minor damage, cope with pain, improve your eyesight, keep out the cold, stay slim for ever, deal with anxiety and even fight against diseases as threatening as cancer.

If you find all this startling it is probably because you have learned to take your body's natural skills for granted.

But just think about some of your body's simplest skills for a moment.

If you cut yourself you expect the blood to clot and the

wound to heal. It doesn't seem like anything special or particularly complicated. In practice, however, the blood clotting mechanism that you take for granted is part of a magnificently sophisticated defence system.

A network of failsafe mechanisms ensures that the system isn't accidentally triggered into action when there is no leak. More safety checks ensure that the clotting system doesn't begin to operate until enough blood has flown through the injury site to wash away any dirt which might be present. Once the clot has formed and the loss of blood has been stopped, the damaged cells will release into the tissues chemicals which are designed to make the local blood vessels expand. The expansion of the vessels ensures that extra quantities of blood flow into the injury site, the additional blood making the area red, swollen and hot. The heat will help damage or kill any infective organisms and the swelling will ensure that the injured part is not used too much. By immobilising the area, the pain and the stiffness will act as a natural splint.

White blood cells brought to the injury site will help by swallowing up any debris or bacteria. These scavenging cells, bloated with rubbish, will allow themselves to be discharged from your body as pus once they have done their job. Then, once the debris has been cleared and the threat of infection removed, the injury will begin to heal. The scar tissue that forms will be stronger than the original skin which it has replaced.   All this assumes that the injury is a fairly small one and that the clotting mechanism can deal with the potential blood loss quickly and easily. If there is a greater blood loss your body has a number of other mechanisms which it can use to help keep you alive.

As a final, added refinement which any engineer would consider a touch of pure genius, any appreciable loss of blood will trigger off a thirst intended to ensure that your missing body fluids are replaced as quickly as possible.

The blood clotting mechanism is just one – and one of the simplest – of hundreds of mechanisms which exist within your body to protect you from harm.

If you go out for the evening and drink several pints of fluid then your kidneys will get rid of the excess. On the other hand if you spend a hot day hiking and you drink very little then your kidneys will reduce your fluid output. While they are regulating the fluid flow your kidneys will also ensure that the salts, electrolytes and other chemicals in your body are kept balanced.

If you've been drinking in a pub and you've eaten too many salted peanuts your body will balance your intake of fluid and salt against your body's needs for these two ingredients.

There are mechanisms which are designed to keep your internal temperature stable. Sit in the sun and your skin will go pink as more fluid flows through the surface vessels of your body. This increase in superficial blood flow will enable your body to get rid of heat simply because the blood will lose heat to the surrounding air, You'll sweat too, as your body cunningly uses the fact that when water evaporates heat is lost. Incidentally, as the sweat pours out, so the amount of saliva you produce will fall, thus making your mouth dry. You will get thirsty and drink more fluids to replace the fluid your body is losing.

Should a speck of dust find its way into one of your eyes, tears will flood out in an attempt to wash the irritant away. The tears contain a special bactericidal substance designed to kill off any infection. Your eyelids will temporarily go into spasm to protect your eyes from further damage.

When you have a fever, the rise in tissue temperature is probably a result of your body trying to help you cope more effectively with any infection that may be present. The temperature rise improves the capacity of your body's defence mechanisms while at the same time threatening the existence of the invading organisms.

Your body's powers are truly extensive and amazing!

Researchers have shown that the human brain contains a natural drug designed to help anxiety, that pain thresholds and pain tolerance levels increase quite naturally during the final days of pregnancy, that breast milk contains a substance designed to tell a baby when he has had enough to eat, and that during the years when a woman is fertile the walls of her vagina produce a special chemical designed to reduce the risk of any local infection developing. Do a lot of kneeling on a hard surface and your knee caps will acquire a soft, squashy, protective swelling. Eat something infected and you will vomit. Get something stuck in your windpipe and you will cough it up. Spend a lot of time in the sun and special pigmented cells will migrate to the surface of your skin to provide you with a layer of protection against the sun's rays.

Your body cannot always cope, of course.

There will be times when even your sophisticated self healing mechanisms will be overwhelmed and will need support.

But to dismiss these mechanisms on the grounds that they don't provide a complete answer to all health problems is like arguing that it isn't worthwhile learning to swim because occasionally you may need the help of a lifeguard.

I firmly believe that if you learn to use the power of your own body you will benefit in a number of ways.

First, of course, you will reduce the risk of being injured by a healthcare professional. Every year thousands of people suffer because of treatments used by orthodox and alternative practitioners. Sometimes a risk is worth taking. Sometimes it isn't. If the alternative is death then obviously a risk is acceptable.

Second, you will benefit because when an interventionist treats an illness he usually tries to oppose your body's own internal responses, as well as whatever outside agent may have triggered those responses in the first place. This isn't necessarily a good idea. All symptoms are merely signs that a fight is taking place inside your body. Unless the interventionist treatment is carefully designed to support and aid the fight the treatment applied may well end up damaging and even weakening your body's internal mechanisms – eventually making you more vulnerable and more reliant on interventionists and their treatments.

Try to be aware of your body's recuperative powers. Learn to use those powers and learn to recognise precisely when you need professional support. Retain overall control of your body and bring in the healers as advisers and technicians.

Once you've mastered the idea of using your body's own healing powers you will find yourself enjoying a freedom that you might otherwise never know.

Coleman's Law

Your body knows best. Learn to listen to it.

CHAPTER FOURTEEN

Never be afraid to say 'I don't know'.

However embarrassed you may be by your ignorance do not succumb to the temptation to lie or to bluff.

Nine times out of ten you will be able to get away with pretending that you know something you don't know.

But on the tenth occasion you will be found out. And the embarrassment you will suffer then will be more destructive and more memorable than any other embarrassment you have ever faced.

Remember that even if you are supposed to be an 'expert' admitting that you don't know something is a sign of strength not weakness.

No one can possibly know everything. The powerful, the wise and the great are always prepared to admit that there are boundaries to their knowledge. Only the weak, the uncertain and the stupid are silly enough to pretend that they know everything.

Never be ashamed to admit that there are still things left for you to learn. There is far more shame (and danger) in intellectual arrogance and conceit than in simple honesty.

Coleman's Law

Saying 'I don't know' is a sign of strength not weakness.

CHAPTER FIFTEEN

If you are to enjoy life fully you must never forget that you are part of a community. However independent you may become you will always be dependent on the people who live around you.

Modern life is so complicated that none of us can survive alone. We rely on other people for our food supplies, to keep our road clear, to provide us with electricity, telephones, water and other essential services. We rely on other people to maintain our motor cars, televisions, refrigerators and other pieces of equipment. We rely on other people to deliver our mail and take away our rubbish.

Sadly, many people forget the extent of their indebtedness to the rest of society. The small suburb which has 'LOCAL RESIDENTS ONLY ALLOWED ON THE BEACH' is forgetting that it needs the facilities provided by the other parts of the town. The workers who hold a city to ransom are forgetting that in our modern towns and cities we are all inter-dependent.

However successful you become try always to remember how important the community is to you. Remember that there is no point in having money to spend if you daren't go into the shopping centre for fear of being mugged. Remember that there is no point in having a smart apartment if you live in a society which has crumbled so much that you have to lock yourself inside and barricade your doors and windows.

Remember, too, that if you don't spend money at your local village shop – and maybe pay a little extra for the privilege – then before long the shop will have disappeared and you will have to travel to the superstore for *all* your requirements. Remember that if you do not support local industries then your life will suffer.

Coleman's Law

There is no point in owning a motor car unless there are roads on which you can drive it.

CHAPTER SIXTEEN

Always try to know and understand the forces which drive you.

Only if you know your own driving forces will you be able to plan your life successfully.

Defining your driving forces is probably easier than you think.

If you feel you need to buy new clothes or a new car ask yourself WHY.

Why do you need new clothes?

To keep you warm?

To impress your friends?

To improve your image?

To get a better job?

Why do you need a new car?

Is your old one unreliable?

Or do you need a new car because your old one isn't big enough or fast enough?

Or do you *want* a new car to impress other people and improve your self image?

If you want to earn more money ask yourself WHY?

What do you need the money for?

Do you want to buy something that you can't afford?

Do you want money so that you can buy yourself freedom in the future?

Re-examine your life regularly.

Go through everything you do and ask yourself WHY?

Remember that the pressure from society is insidious and often difficult to spot.

Remember that toxic stress is there all the time – even when you aren't aware that it is there.

Much of the malaise caused by toxic stress is produced by people being pressurised (usually unknowingly and subtly) into doing things that other people want them to do.

Remember that you can reduce your vulnerability to toxic stress but that toxic stress will never go away completely.

To control your own life and reduce the damage done by toxic stress reassess your priorities as often as you can. Carefully and deliberately ask yourself what you want out of life. And carefully and deliberately ask yourself whether the things you are doing are helping you to achieve your aims.

How much do you want the things that more money will buy you?

Is the price you will have to pay too high?

Try to decide what things – and experiences – give you most pleasure and satisfaction.

Then try to decide whether you are driving yourself in the right direction.

Do you obtain real joy from obtaining more status and power?

What gives you *most* pleasure: having money in the bank or watching a beautiful sunset?

What gives you *most* pleasure: a simple picnic or an expensive meal in a fashionable restaurant?

What gives you *most* pleasure: being good at something or receiving public acclaim?

What gives you *most* pleasure: beating someone else or conquering a personal weakness?

Consider all these things carefully. Look constantly at the way you live your life. Understand the forces, desires and ambitions which drive you onwards.

Ask yourself frequently: 'Am I doing the right thing?'

And never forget that if you aren't doing the right thing then you're doing the wrong thing.

Coleman's Law

Only when you know *why* you do things will you know whether they're worth doing.

77

CHAPTER SEVENTEEN

Protect, guard and value your independence.

You will find that few things are easier to part with or harder to regain. Your independence is your intellectual virginity and you should respect it and clutch it tightly to your bosom.

You will find that there are many, many people in the world who will willingly pay you well for your independence. Countries, organisations and companies will all delight in paying you a good price for your independence.

Resist them and their entreaties as you would resist the entreaties of the devil for your soul.

While you still possess your independence they will treat you with caution and respect. They will be courteous and thoughtful, generous and even honourable.

But once they have bought your independence and they own your spirit then they will treat you with contempt. They will tell you how to live your life; they will tell you what to wear; they will tell you how to behave; they will tell you what is honest and what is not honest and they will expect you to be obedient and unquestioning.

Beware of their wiles and their deceits; beware of the subtle ways in which they will endeavour to purchase your independence from you.

Do not let them own you by making you promises, by allowing you to fall into debt with them, by praising you or by rewarding you with status or authority. Beware of your weaknesses and your ambitions; they will use these to worm their way into your soul.

Protect yourself by being loyal only to people, never to

organisations.

And never allow yourself to be persuaded to betray your friends, your loves or your principles for the sake of your country or your company. Once you betray these simple truths your independence is lost for ever. Never sell your soul in the public interest. Do not allow yourself to be tricked into parting with your integrity on the grounds that you are behaving in a public spirited way

Take pride in being your own person.

When your independence goes you lose everything that should be dear to you.

Coleman's Law

Take pride in, and protect, your independence, self respect and dignity.

CHAPTER EIGHTEEN

No one can be right all the time. Everyone make mistakes.

Give yourself strength by being prepared to say: 'I was wrong. I am sorry.'

If you retain an open mind, if you are constantly learning and if you listen to the wisdom of those you respect then you will inevitably change you mind and alter your views as the months and years go by.

Be prepared to say: 'I was wrong. I am sorry.'

If you accept challenges, take risks and live your life to the full then sometimes you will fail. Occasionally your judgements will be faulty. You – and those who have supported you – will lose face.

Be prepared to say : 'I was wrong. I am sorry.'

Making a mistake is a weakness, it is true.

And you should try to make sure that you make as few as possible.

But admitting that you have made a mistake is a sign of strength and courage.

Coleman's Law

Apologising for your mistakes is a sign of maturity and strength. Learning from your mistakes is a sign of true wisdom.

CHAPTER NINETEEN

Beware of hate. It is a destructive and damaging emotion.

The cruel irony is that although your hatred will rarely harm the person who has done you wrong it may kill you.

If you cannot forgive try to forget.

The longer you nurse a hate the more you will damage your physical and mental health.

Coleman's Law

Hate usually does more damage to the person doing the hating than to the object of their hatred.

CHAPTER TWENTY

You may never become rich but there are two things that you can offer people for which they will always be grateful.

Remember these two things and you will never be alone, never be without friends, never be without influence and never be without joy.

The first thing you can give to people is a smile. A *real* smile.

If you smile at someone he will like you. He may not know why. He may not *want* to like you . But he will feel himself warming to you. He will want to please you – and see more of your smile – and so he will do things which you like.

Everyone wants to please other people. It is a natural and understandable human emotion.

And a smile is the key that unlocks happiness.

Watch a mother with her child. Watch two lovers. Watch a salesman with a customer.

They all smile at one another.

There's a bonus for you if you smile at other people. You'll feel better yourself too. Try it now. Try smiling. Nothing conquers sadness, boredom or irritation as effectively as a smile.

The second way to influence people and make friends is to remember to say 'thank you' when it is appropriate.

Not long ago I attended a massive, international conference. It was a huge success. Delegates had flown in from all over the world and they were delighted with all the arrangements. The lectures were useful and informative. The hotel accommodation was excellent. The food was delicious. and the evening entertainment were well planned and brilliantly executed.

The whole conference had been organised by a professional

conference company. But a fairly junior executive of the sponsoring company had been given the job of liasing with the conference organisers. He had worked day and night for six months to ensure that everything was a success. His marriage had been put under an extraordinary strain.

On the last evening of the conference I found the young executive in a dark corner of the hotel bar. He was alone and quietly and efficiently getting drunk.

When I asked him what the matter was and why he wasn't joining in the final evening celebrations he told me that he was thinking of leaving his company. He said he never wanted to see the chairman of his company again.

Knowing that the directors had been extremely pleased with the executive's work – and that they all felt that the conference had been a great success – I was surprised. I asked him why he felt so low.

'I've just been given my next assignment,' the executive sobbed into his brandy. 'The chairman wants me to help set up a new Overseas Marketing Unit. Its a good job I guess. And I'm getting a pay rise and a bigger car. But I've just put six months of my life into this conference and I didn't even get a 'thank you'.'

That was what was hurting.

No one had bothered to say 'Thank you.'

The lesson is surely a simple one.

Nothing, no reward and no amount of money, can replace a quiet, old fashioned, honest and well meant 'Thank you.'

Remember these two things and your life will be blessed with friendship, companionship and happiness.

Coleman's Law

However good your life is it will be better if you smile and say 'thank you' more often.

CHAPTER TWENTY-ONE

Modern technology means that your world is probably full of second hand sensations and hollow imitations of reality. Thanks to television you can sit in your living room and watch other people exploring jungles, seas, mountains tops and other planets. You can sit in your favourite armchair and watch men scrambling through pot holes, venturing into volcanoes and stepping across the moon.

Thanks to the imaginations and skills of theme park builders you can visit bizarre fairy tale castles peopled by cartoon characters without ever having to travel more than a few hundred yards away from a burger bar.

You can sit in comfort and watch other people playing dangerous, competitive games. You can watch the best sportsmen in the world – apparently for free – on your television.

Society wants you to take advantage of all these imitation sensations. When you're watching other people play sport you're spending money. When you're watching other people play sport you're spending money. When you're visiting a theme park you're spending money. When you're watching television you are also watching advertisements – and supporting the consumer age.

But do not allow society to seduce you into totally abandoning real experiences in the real world.

Watching an explorer battling through South American jungles may be good television but no two dimensional experience on a screen can begin to match the joy you can derive from a real life walk alongside a real life river.

Television cannot and will not satisfy the myriad senses of the mind or the spirit.

The most dramatic television adventure can never compete with the simplest real experience.

Try to experience as many different things as you can. Try out things for yourself. Don't accept a life of second hand experiences and second hand pleasures. You gain much, much more from a real game of tennis, golf or football that you play yourself than from watching professionals exhibiting their skills.

However good they may be second hand sensations are no substitute for the real thing.

Coleman's Law

A modest first hand experience always beats a spectacular second hand experience.

CHAPTER TWENTY-TWO

Humility and self effacement are often regarded as virtues. And in many respects they are. But the shy and selfless often find that they are used and put upon by their more aggressive friends and neighbours.

Never forget that although too much assertiveness can easily be mistaken for aggression, a little assertiveness is good for your mind and your body.

Thousands of people who are unable or unwilling to assert themselves are pushed around by parents, family, friends, relatives, employers, doctors and just about everyone else they meet. Their lives are run by others. They find themselves doing errands for other people who could perfectly well run their own errands. They find themselves stuck with dull, boring, administrative chores that no one else wants. They find themselves lumbered with looking after the children while everyone else goes off to have a good time at a party. They find themselves accepting dinner invitations that they would really like to refuse. They find themselves being pushed into buying things they don't really want.

Things reach a dismal peak in hospital. There the unassertive patient will be put to bed, in pyjamas, and will stay there, confined and bound to conform. The patient who doesn't like to speak out will do what he is told when he is told to do it.

Doctors and nurses like their patients to be unassertive because it makes the hospital easier to run. If all the patients keep still and don't ask too many questions it makes life very easy for the staff. But the evidence shows that seriously ill patients who do not assert themselves are the patients who are the first to die. The patients who are considered 'model patients' and who are liked by doctors and nurses for their docility are the ones who don't survive

The patients who survive are the ones who demand information, who refuse to be dominated, who write down questions they want answered, who want to be moved into a better position, who can't accept administrative nonsense just because everyone else accepts it, who want to know the reason behind every test and procedure: the patients who, in short, have the temerity to stick up for themselves as individuals. Doctors and nurses may occasionally find such patients tiresome but it is these, assertive, patients who get better quicker and who *survive*!

The hospital situation is a rather special one, of course. But outside hospital there are many, many ways in which you will suffer if you do not learn to stick up for yourself and stand up for your rights. As well as being physically and mentally worn out from doing chores for other people you will risk encountering frustration and anger as you struggle to stifle your sense of outrage and discomfort at being used.

The feelings of frustration suffered by the non-assertive can be immense and extremely destructive, producing a wide range of physical and mental problems. Headaches and stomach pains are, for example, just two of the many common physical consequences of allowing yourself to be 'used'.

Surprisingly, perhaps, it is remarkably easy to become assertive. You don't have to be aggressive, rude or unpleasant. You simply have to be more aware of your own needs and wishes and more prepared to stand your own ground when you are put under pressure by others who want you to behave in a way that satisfies *them*.

Naturally, you won't always get your own way. That's not what being assertive is all about! But by establishing your preferences, by making it clear that you have your own likes and dislikes, by showing that you are an individual and by standing up for yourself you will help yourself to stay healthier; you will gain enormously from the greater self respect that you acquire and from the benefits of spending less time on things – or with people – that you positively dislike.

Remember to be as straightforward and as honest as you

can be. If you don't want to do something then say so! If you try to offer excuses or complex explanations you'll probably end up trapping yourself in a corner from which escape is impossible.

If you feel embarrassed, self conscious or even ashamed of trying to do things *your* way, help yourself by trying to put yourself into the position of an outside observer. Many people who are unassertive fail to look after themselves effectively because they are frightened of how they will appear to other people. But if you do put yourself in someone else's shoes you'll almost certainly find that your behaviour really isn't as terrible as you thought it was. Stop and think about what you are doing, try to be dispassionate, and you'll probably realise that your behaviour is entirely responsible.

Coleman's Law

Stick up for yourself. If you don't then the chances are than no one else will.

CHAPTER TWENTY-THREE

One of the bravest, most difficult but ultimately most rewarding things you have to learn to do is to trust your instincts.

As the weeks, months and years go by you will gradually acquire a strange sixth sense. Your natural, inborn sense of intuition will develop and you will get to know when something seems 'right' or 'wrong'.

But, sadly, you will also discover that many people suppress or are frightened to acknowledge their own personal judgements.

More than at any other time in the history of mankind we live in a world which is dominated by experts. Politicians always excuse their decisions (and especially their mistakes) by blaming the experts. Many of the political and social policies which turn out to be irrational, purposeless, vindictive, prejudiced or just plain wrong were originally devised and enthusiastically endorsed by experts.

Do not be afraid to stand by your feelings; never assume that the experts always know what they are talking about; don't be tricked or seduced into believing that the decisions made on behalf of society are right or rational.

Modern experts, the people who mould the decisions which will shape the world in which you live are usually unelected, unseen, anonymous, uncontrolled and, it seems, beyond criticism. Strangely, however often they may be wrong they will never lose their expert status.

Time and time again you will see that the most damaging and most destructive decisions are made by, or under the guidance of, people who regard themselves as experts.

Instead of suppressing or ignoring your natural intuitive

skills and your natural understanding of what is right and what is wrong you should endeavour to sharpen your skills and learn to use them as often as you can.

You can start with small things.

Look around you and you'll see that many people, apparently well educated, sensible, sane, knowledgeable people, find it difficult to make relatively simple decisions.

Watch a diner in a restaurant trying to decide what to choose from the menu. Watch a man or woman in his or her bedroom trying to decide what to wear.

Time and time again you'll see people creating stress and anxiety for themselves. You'll see him worrying about whether to wear the blue suit with the red tie or the grey suit with the blue tie. You'll see her suffering agonies as she tries to decide whether to wear the black shoes or the red shoes.

You can hone your instinctive skills *and* save yourself from these myriad anxieties by training yourself to make such relatively simple and trivial decisions within minutes. Learn to make up your mind to follow whatever thought springs first to your mind. If your first instinct was to wear the blue then wear the blue. Don't waste mental energy thinking about it. If your first instinct is to choose the fish then choose the fish. Force yourself to think quickly and decisively; to assess the options speedily. You'll suffer far fewer regrets and liberate yourself from much unnecessary anxiety.

If you find yourself facing a more difficult problem – and you simply cannot find the answer – give up and do something completely different. Take a walk or a warm, relaxing bath. Or sit down in front of the fire with a good book. Allow your subconscious mind to work on the problem, and to assess the various options, and you will soon find that there is but one clear solution. The more you do this the more your instinctive, intuitive skills will develop.

Gradually, learn to trust your instincts when the stakes are higher. Learn to listen to your inner self and you will find a peace and a calm that most people will never be able to share. Learn to say and do what you think is right and to act in the way that makes you feel comfortable. Don't allow yourself to be pressurised by the expectations or exhortations of society or its accursed experts.

Coleman's Law

Don't be afraid to listen to your instincts. They're probably right.

CHAPTER TWENTY-FOUR

Don't let other people push you into doing things you don't want to do by telling you that you are indispensable.

And don't force yourself into taking on responsibilities which damage your health and your happiness by accepting the myth of indispensability.

Society likes people to feel that they are indispensable. It makes them work harder.

But the truth is that however good you are at something you will never be indispensable.

If you die the world will go on. Nothing will stop.

If you want to find out how important and how indispensable you are try this simple experiment.

Fill a bowl with cold water.

Now dip your hand into the bowl for thirty seconds.

Then pull your hand out of the water again.

And look at the size of the hole that is left when your hand is removed.

That's how indispensable you are.

Coleman's Law

Graveyards are full of people who were indispensable.

CHAPTER TWENTY-FIVE

Fear of the unknown is a powerful driving force. Fear is likely to keep you busy doing a job you don't like because you're frightened of what might happen if you leave. Fears keep people in relationships which have no future. Fear destroys courage and initiative. Fear of the unknown is one of society's ways of keeping you under control.

You can conquer this fear by making a determined effort to use your imagination to help you discover the worst that can happen. The ironic truth is that the worst that is likely to happen is usually nowhere near as bad as you might fear.

A woman I know suffered a lot with her nerves. Most of her problems were a result of the job she did. She found the work unpleasant and stressful. She didn't like the man she worked for. But she had worked at the same place for fifteen years and she was frightened of what would happen if she lost her job.

She assumed that if she lost her job she would starve to death. She had never really thought what would happen. But she had always assumed that she needed her boss far more than he needed her. That was, or course, partly his fault. He wanted her to feel that way. He was able to use her fear to get her to work for long hours at a dull job for low pay.

She was a classic victim of the society in which we all live. And she was a chronic sufferer from toxic stress.

One day I managed to persuade her to sit down and carefully examine her greatest fear; what would happen if she lost her job.

She was vulnerable because society had taught her to be frightened of the unknown and because society had encouraged her to believe that she should dedicate herself to her job without thinking of herself.

She felt frightened at the prospect of surviving alone and she felt guilty at the thought of abandoning her job.

But the more the thought about it the more she realised that the unknown she feared wasn't really all that terrifying. She realised that she had numerous well sought after skills. By looking in the 'appointments' section of the local newspaper she discovered that there were plenty of firms advertising for people like her. She realised that her experience and knowledge more than outweighed her age as far as other potential employers were concerned.

She found the bottom line.

And she realised that it wasn't as frightening as she had feared.

She applied for another, better paid job that looked more fun.

She got it.

And she handed in her notice.

Her boss, suddenly realising that he needed her, offered to increase her salary by over one third. He offered her better holidays and an annual bonus.

But she wasn't interested. She didn't want to work for him. She left. And she did so with a light heart as she realised that *he* needed her far more than *she* needed him.

If you have any terrible fear which haunts you try to confront it. And try to define the bottom line. Try to work out what is the worst that can happen.

You will probably surprise yourself. Once you know the bottom line you'll find that you can relax far more than when you are worrying about the unknown.

There are very few problems or threats in your life that will actually stop your world going round.

Coleman's Law

The bottom line is hardly ever as bad as you think its going to be.

94

CHAPTER TWENTY-SIX

Regardless of what society expects you to do try to spend as much of your life as possible doing things that you enjoy.

Try to find work that you enjoy. It may not pay as well to start with but you'll do it better and probably be more successful at it. And you'll certainly have more fun.

Remember that work doesn't have to be dull. And you don't have to spend your life doing dull things.

Society would like you to do dull things. Society wants you to be dull. Dull people work harder and spend their money trying to become happy. Society needs people to work hard, have dull lives and spend plenty of money on a search for pleasure.

Coleman's Law

The more you enjoy something the more likely you are to be successful at it.

CHAPTER TWENTY-SEVEN

Do not allow anyone to persuade you that pride is always a sin. It is not.

You should have pride in your honesty, your integrity and your independence.

You should have pride in your skills, your achievements and your strengths.

You should have pride in your family, your friends and your community.

Pride will give you courage, determination and fire. Pride will give you the power to fight injustice and cruelty.

Pride is only a sin when it leads to arrogance, vanity, and a contempt for others.

Coleman's Law

Pride in yourself, your skills and your achievements will give you the strength to fight toxic stress and to overcome The Twentieth Century Blues.

CHAPTER TWENTY-EIGHT

Money is, for many people, almost as important as life itself. It is the lubricant which helps to turn the wheels of industry and stands in the place of joy, happiness, love, friendship and contentment.

Right from the start you must learn to regard money with the right mixture of respect and contempt. You must have respect for the ways in which it can help you – and the ways in which it can help you improve the world – but you must have contempt for the ways in which it can encourage the weak spirited to part with their integrity, their honesty and their courage.

Contrary to what you will hear the most important things that money can buy you are not material possessions. The greatest power of money is not that it can buy land or houses or cars but that it can buy you time and freedom. Money cannot buy you happiness or contentment but it can buy you the opportunity to explore your personal strengths and capabilities. Money can buy you freedom from drudgery and can free you from the time clock.

Never allow money to rise above its proper station. Do not allow money to acquire control of your life.

In the past radicals and revolutionaries have often made the mistake of trying to create revolutions out of a sense of material injustice. They have encouraged their followers to fight for more money and have instantly played into the hands of the establishment. Once a man demands more money he is putting a price on his life and starting negotiations that he must lose. Once a man learns to negotiate exclusively about money then he loses his position of strength.

Learn to put money in its place.

When negotiating the extent of your next compensation package remember to fight for better safer working conditions; to campaign for more interesting work, a chance to learn more and educate yourself, to enhance your skills and a chance to contribute more. Remember to fight for a better life.

Remember that money can't buy you love but it can buy you time to fall in love and the freedom to enjoy love when you've found it.

If you manage to save a little money don't think you have to rush out and spend it.

Put it in the bank, earning good interest, and forget about it. Put it somewhere secure where you can get hold of it when you need it.

Society wants you to spend your money. If you spend every penny you earn then you will help society to get richer. And if you spend your money then you will remain tied to your job and to the system.

But if you have a little money put aside then you can buy yourself freedom. With a little money in the bank you will find it easier to say 'no' when you want to say 'no'. You will find it easier to walk away when people want you to do things you don't want to do. You will find it easier to control your own life.

Money can't buy you love but it can buy you freedom. Freedom is, in fact, the most valuable commodity that money can buy you.

Coleman's Law

Don't let money ruin your life. Use it to make your life better.

CHAPTER TWENTY-NINE

A stone cutter will hammer a piece of rock one hundred times without anything happening.

After the 101st blow the rock will split easily and cleanly in two.

The 101st blow was no different to the blows that went before it.

You cannot see the effect of those first one hundred blows.

Until after the 101st blow has been struck.

Coleman's Law

If you really want something never give up trying.

CHAPTER THIRTY

If you want to succeed at something then you must have faith in yourself. You must believe in yourself. You must be able to 'see' yourself doing what it is that you want to do.

Men have been trying to see how fast they can run a mile for as long as the measurement has existed. And men have been trying to run a mile in under four minutes since the five minute barrier was broken.

For years thousands of athletes tried to beat the four minute barrier.

And failed.

And then an athlete called Roger Bannister succeeded.

The year *after* Bannister had proved that the impossible was possible 30 other runners completed the mile in under four minutes.

And the year after that 300 runners broke the four minute barrier.

Nothing had changed. A mile was still as long as ever. And four minutes was still 240 seconds. But suddenly the impossible had become the possible.

Coleman's Law

If you really want something then you must believe in your ability to get it. If you think you're going to fail then you'll almost certainly fail. If you think you can succeed then you'll stand a chance of succeeding.

CHAPTER THIRTY-ONE

Don't let other people waste your time – or trick you into wasting your money because you believe they have wasted *their* time because of you.

Salesman selling double glazing, new kitchens and motor cars will squander their time on you if you let them. They will spend hours with you. They will talk about their product, your hobbies, your job, their boss, the weather and the state of the potato crop in Ireland.

They want to waste your time.

And they want you to waste their time.

Because they know that the longer you spend together the more likely you are to buy something you don't want (and probably can't afford).

After a couple of hours you will feel bad if you say 'no'. You'll be conscious of the fact that you've wasted a great deal of your own time. And you'll be conscious of the fact that you've wasted a great deal of their time.

So you'll sign a contract.

If you want to buy something ask the salesman to tell you the facts about his product in five minutes. And tell him to leave his brochures for you to look at. Tell him that he must leave after five minutes or else you will not do business with him. And mean it.

If you don't want to buy what he has to sell then tell him that. Don't waste your time allowing him to ask you questions designed to trick you into starting a conversation. Don't allow him to say anything.

Remember that he is prepared to squander his time for some of your money. But you will be expected to squander both you money *and* your time!

And remember how hard you have to work for every hour of your free time that the salesman is so willing to squander for you.

Coleman's Law

Look after the minutes as carefully as you look after the pennies and the hours, like the pounds, will look after themselves.

CHAPTER THIRTY-TWO

Vanity is a powerful, natural phenomenon. It is sensible and good that we should take pride in our appearance, our intelligence and our success.

But the vanity that is likely to cripple you is not natural.

During the last twenty to thirty years advertising agencies have discovered that by appealing to your vanity they can sell you all sorts of things that you don't really need.

(You may think that I am exaggerating the importance of advertising but let me remind you of two things: first, that the vast majority of the messages you will see during your lifetime will be inspired and paid for by people who want to sell you something and second, that many of the messages which are not specifically paid for by advertisers will still be influenced by them. We live in the communications age and the best and most powerful communications are advertisers.)

When you get up in the morning you wash yourself in a special, expensive soap that the manufacturers tell you will help you to smell fresher. Just in case that doesn't work you then smother yourself in cologne.

You choose your clothes for the day carefully. Fashion will play as a big part in what you decide to put on as will the weather.

While you're getting dressed you check your hair for grey streaks and your face for wrinkles.

And so it goes on throughout the day. Just about everything you do is determined not by what you really want but what you think you ought to do in order to avoid embarrassing yourself or offending other people.

Your fears of offending other people or embarrassing yourself have been carefully built up by advertisers who have turned small, natural vanities into huge anxieties from which they can make massive profits.

It is vanity – boosted by clever advertising – that encourages us to try and get fit without exercising properly, to try and get slim without cutting down on our consumption of fattening foods and to try and educate ourselves without having to spend long, boring hours studying.

It is our manufactured vanity that enables dress designers, cosmetics manufacturers and plastic surgeons to make vast fortunes out of their modest skills. It is our manufactured vanity that enables car manufacturers to persuade us to replace perfectly good vehicles with ever more expensive models.

It is our manufactured vanity that enables an endless stream of companies and professionals to convince us that in order to satisfy our inner needs and to repel our insecurities we must spend our money on the products they make and the services they provide.

There are several things that you can do to protect yourself from the greedy hordes who are desperate to build up your vanity and to take advantage of your manufactured fears.

First, and most important, you should make a careful and comprehensive list of all your virtues, skills and talents. Our manufactured vanities are built upon feelings of mental and physical inadequacy. Write down all your good points and you will strengthen your resistance.

Begin with the physical. Whether you are tall or small, stocky or skinny, there will always be good points that you can be proud of. Even if you are genuinely overweight (virtually a sin in our society) remember that some of the most attractive people in history have been plump.

Then think of the mental skills and expertise you have. Try writing an advertisement for yourself extolling your own virtues. Once you stop and think about it you'll probably be amazed to see just how many virtues you have got. If you're shy, lacking in self confidence and vulnerable to manufactured vanities you're probably also unusually honest, generous, thoughtful and hard working. You're probably also punctual, careful, kind and unusually creative.

Next time you're feeling low, inferior and vulnerable think of your virtues.

Second, if you suspect that you worry unduly about your appearance and you are constantly tempted to spend more than you can possibly afford on clothes, hairdressers and other image makers then try to see yourself as other see you.

Do you really shun people who wear last year's fashions? Do you really despise everyone who has a darn in a jumper? Do you refuse to mix with people whose hair is less than perfect? Do you judge your friends according to the cost of their shoes? Of course you don't. So why should you assume that other people will judge you in that way?

The simple truth is that your idea of what other people expect is coloured not by reality nor by experience but by advertisements. When you feel that you must get rid of your old suit and buy a new one simply because the cut is slightly dated you are responding to pressures deliberately exerted by parts of society which want to make money out of you. Your vanity is inspired not by commonsense but by false fears inspired by skilful copywriters.

Society needs you to keep spending long after your personal needs have been satisfied.

Finally, remember that humour is vanity's most powerful enemy. Try not to take yourself too seriously. Remember that without your vanity flattery and commercial blackmail will never work. And when next you find yourself being influenced by vanity ask yourself if what you are doing is inspired by a genuine, personal concern or an artificial and commercially inspired concern for what complete strangers might think!

Coleman's Law

Vanity is strengthened by false assumptions about the expectations of others; it is weakened by self confidence, honesty and humour.

CHAPTER THIRTY-THREE

Do not listen to the people who tell you that you are powerless.

They are wrong.

It is true that many of those who have power over you – large institutions, the police, the politicians and so on – have little regard for your rights.

But you have more power than you realise.

First, and most important, you have the power to decide when, what and how much you consume.

Every advertisement you see and every exhortation you hear will be designed to encourage you to buy and to spend. Only if you constantly buy and spend will the money be created to oil the wheels of industry and commerce. It is your buying and your spending that gives them the money to have power over you. It is your buying and your spending that give you the debts that puts you in their power.

By resisting the temptations to buy and spend more than you need or want you will be reducing their power and building up your own.

Once you have mastered the desire to over consume you will have freed yourself from their tyrannical rule.

Remember that no one will build cars which damage the environment if no one buys them. Remember that as a consumer and an employee you have the ultimate power. If you don't agree with the way that a company pollutes the environment or treats its employees do not buy its products. And do what you can to persuade your friends to boycott its products too. The company will soon learn. If you don't agree with the way that the company you work for pollutes the environment or treats its other employees express your disapproval. Let them know that you are unhappy. The worst they can do is sack you. But do you really want to work for a company which does not care for the things you care for? If you have reduced your susceptibility to advertising and limited your expenditure as a consumer then you will be free to use your power of disapproval to guide the company for which you work.

Make sure the politicians hear you too. Let them know when they do things of which you disapprove.

Don't just sit back and say 'there's nothing I can do'.

That simply isn't true.

Politicians – like big companies – are frightened of you. They need your support. If you make it clear that you disapprove of what they do then they will try harder to please you.

Remember that you are not alone. No one wants poor housing. No one wants people to starve to death. No one wants inadequate health care. No one wants to see the environment ruined.

Remember that society can only get away with doing things you find offensive if you let it get away with it.

Coleman's Law

You have all the power in the world. It is up to you to decide how and when to use it.

POSTSCRIPT

One further, final thought. Don't add more toxic stress to your life by trying to do too much to soon. Move at a pace you feel comfortable with. Do what you can, when you can. Remember, the principles and laws in this book are designed to reduce the stress in your life – not to add to it!

WHAT READERS SAY ABOUT
VERNON COLEMAN

Here are a few comments from Vernon Coleman's thousands of readers:

'I always read his column with the greatest interest' – Mrs Edwina Currie, M.P., Parliamentary Under-Secretary of State for Health and Social Security speaking at the House of Commons.

'I would like to thank you for telling us the truth' – R.K. Kent.

'I feel I must write and congratulate you ... your no-nonsense attitude, teamed with plain common sense makes a refreshing change from some articles written today. Please keep up the good work' – L.B., Leicestershire.

'Thanks over and over again – good health always to you as you are fighting for a good cause in life – for the sick' – E.H., Cleveland.

'I only wish to God that we had a few such as your good self in Parliament, then maybe our standard of life would possibly be better' – H. H., Somerset.

'I must admit that initially I thought that some of your ideas were extreme, but sadly I must concede that I was wrong' – C.D., Surrey

'Every time I see you on T.V. I get such a lift to the spirits' – B.D., Humberside.

'I greatly admire your no nonsense approach to things and your acting as champion of the people' – L.A., Cornwall

'I have now read and studied all your excellent books and have enjoyed and benefited from them immensely' – B.B., Dorset.

'Your no nonsense approach to the medical profession is a tonic in itself – C.S., Tyne and Wear.

'May I say that I think you have done a real service to all those who have the sense and patience to study your books' – B.A., Hampshire.

'I admire your courage to speak out for what you believe to be the truth' – E.C., Northants.

'Your words and smiling face really cheered me up and made my day. I intend doing *exactly* as you said' – A.A., Suffolk.